I Can Read...

Snow White

Once upon a time there was
a beautiful girl called Snow White.
Her father was the King and her
stepmother was the Queen.
The Queen had a magic mirror.

This book belongs to:

sarah Meree

victoreen lilee un Evans

Reading Together

This story is written in a special way so that a child and an adult can 'take turns' in reading the text.

The left hand side is for the adult to read.

The Queen sent Snow White out into the woods with a huntsman.
The Queen told the huntsman to kill Snow White. But the huntsman felt sorry for Snow White. He did not kill her.
The huntsman let Snow White run away.

The huntsman let Snow White run away.

The right hand side has a simple sentence (taken from the story) which the child reads.

Firstly, it is always helpful to read the whole book to your child, stopping to talk about the pictures. Explain that you are going to read it again but this time the child can join in.

Read the left hand page and when you come to the sentence which is repeated on the other page run your finger under this. Your child then tries to read the same sentence opposite.

Searching for the child's sentence in the adult version is a useful activity. Your child will have a real sense of achievement when all the sentences on the right hand page can be read. Giving lots of praise is very important.

Enjoy the story together.

The Queen had a magic mirror.

Every day, the Queen looked in the
mirror and said,
"Mirror Mirror on the wall, who is the
fairest of them all?"
Every day the mirror replied,
"You are the fairest of them all."
But one day the magic mirror said,
"Snow White is the fairest of them all."
The Queen was very angry.

The Queen was very angry.

The Queen sent Snow White out into
the woods with a huntsman.
The Queen told the huntsman to kill
Snow White. But the huntsman felt sorry
for Snow White. He did not kill her.
The huntsman let Snow White run away.

The huntsman let Snow White
run away.

Snow White ran into the woods.
She found a little house.
Snow White went into the house.
Inside there were seven little beds.
Snow White fell asleep on one of the beds.
When Snow White woke up she saw
seven dwarves.

Snow White fell asleep on one of the beds.

The dwarves said, "This is our house.
What are you doing here?"
"I am frightened," said Snow White.
Snow White asked the dwarves to
help her.
The dwarves said that Snow White could
live in their house.
They all lived happily together.

Snow White asked the dwarves
to help her.

The Queen thought Snow White
was dead.
She said, "Mirror mirror on the wall,
who is the fairest of them all?"
The magic mirror said, "Snow White
is still the fairest of them all!"
The Queen was very angry.

The Queen thought Snow White
was dead.

The Queen put a magic spell on an apple.
The Queen dressed up as an old lady.
She went into the woods.
She knocked on the door of the little house.
Snow White opened the door.

The Queen put a magic spell
on an apple.

The Queen gave the apple to Snow White.
Snow White bit the apple. She fell down.
It was as if she was dead.
The Queen was very happy.

The Queen gave the apple to
Snow White.

The dwarves put Snow White into
a glass coffin.

One day a handsome prince rode by.

The prince thought Snow White was
very beautiful.

The prince kissed Snow White.

The prince kissed Snow White.

Snow White woke up.
She was not dead after all.
The wicked Queen ran away and was
never seen again.
Snow White and the prince lived happily
ever after. So did the seven dwarves.

Snow White woke up.

Key Words

Can you read these words and find them in the book?

Snow White

apple

King

Queen

dwarves

Questions and Answers

Now that you've read the story can you answer these questions?

a. Who had a
magic mirror?

b. What kind of fruit
did the Queen put
a spell on?

c. Who kissed
Snow White?

a. The Queen   b. An apple   c. The Prince

Tell your own Story

Can you make up a different story with the pictures and words below?

horse

mirror

run

cottage

dwarves

Queen

King

woods

Mix and Match

Draw a line from the pictures to the correct word to match them up.

King

mirror

Queen

Snow White

dwarves

apple

CELEBRATING 90 YEARS OF NAAFI
SERVING THE SERVICES

The Navy, Army & Air Force Institutes

This book is based on the 75 Year Anniversary book 'NAAFI Up' which in
turn was based on an original anniversary concept by Chris Clifton-Moore;
we gratefully acknowledge this and thank all of its contributors.

PUBLICATION TEAM

NAAFI
Lee Coleman, Lisa Muxlow & Andrew Smart

Design
Air Creative Marketing Ltd

Print
St Ives Westerham Press Ltd

PUBLISHED BY

The Navy, Army & Air Force Institutes
Suite 4-6, The Beehive, Lingfield Point
McMullen Road, Darlington
County Durham. DL1 1YN
©2010

www.naafi.co.uk
ISBN 978-0-9567305-0-3

In March 1920 Winston Churchill, then Secretary of State for War, set up a committee to advise on the kind of canteen organisation which would be needed for the Armed Forces in the future.

The findings were unanimous; there should be one organisation to serve all three Services, it should be permanent and it should be able to rapidly expand or contract at times of war or peace. The Navy, Army and Air Force Institutes was therefore established on 6th December 1920 and started trading as NAAFI in 1921.

As a not for profit organisation, with no shareholders to reward, NAAFI was asked to provide catering, retail and leisure wherever needed, around the world.

90 years on, we're still dedicated to 'Serving the Services'.

IN MEMORY OF MORE THAN 550 NAAFI STAFF
WHO MADE THE ULTIMATE SACRIFICE FOR THEIR
COUNTRY AND LOST THEIR LIVES SO BRAVELY
SERVING THE SERVICES

YOUR COURAGE AND COMMITMENT
WILL ALWAYS BE REMEMBERED
AND NEVER FORGOTTEN

Robert Arthur Adams   Joseph Agius   Joseph Agius   Frank Richard Aldis   Henry Charles Aldridge   Herbert Montague Ernest Aldridge   Alfred Kenneth Algute...

Frank Allen   Seth Henry Allen   Harry Ascroft   Frank Stanley Ash   Fredrick Charles Ashby   George Geoffrey Ashby   Gordon Edward Ashworth   Arthur Robert Aston

Frank Reuben Ayling   Leslie George Ayling   Stanley John Arthur Bagge   Denis Baker   Frederick James Baldwin   Herbert Victor Barling   Charles Henry Patrick Barnes

William Earnest Barritt   Rex Edmund Barry   Emmanuel Bartolo   Alfred James Batt   Richard Bayliss   Frederich Charles Bee   Alfred Frank Beer   Michael Beirne

William Hunt Bellenger   Reginald Sidney John Bendall   Thomas William Beveridge   Stanley Bewick   Frederick Arthur Bird   Thomas Mutter Birrell

Edward George Bishop   Hilary Bishop   William Black   Joan Boddinor   Alexander Bolton   Joseph Bonello   John Frederick Bontoft   George Bower

ohn Boylan   William Boyle   John Brabner   Harry Brand   Joseph William Brann   George Bray   Harry Brettell   Forster Anderson Brewis   William George Brickle...

Donald Albert Brierley   Basil Arthur Briggs   Reginald Charles Britton   Francis Joseph Brookhouse   Alice Brown   Thomas William Brown   Montague Eric Browne

ames Wilfred...man   Andrew Archibald Burgon   Brian Lonsdale Burke   Frank Philip Burn   Henry Burne   Henry James Burns   Edith Burnville

Reginald Burton   Frederick John Buskell   Albert David Butler   Vincent Cahill   Arthur James Cail   Alec Leonard Campbell   Alexander McLuckie Campbel...

Reginald Mumford Campbell   Augustine Carbone   Mathew Kiddie Carnegie   Robert Ravera Carr   Joseph Cassar   Charles Caygill   Norman Victor Chamberlain

Percy William Chandler   Cyril James Chedzóy   Thomas Joseph Cheevers   Arthur Edwin Childs   James Chilton   Lawrence Chircop   Carmelo Ciappara   Andrew Hubert Clark

Alfred Aldred Clarke   Cyril Thomas Clarke   Jack Cleave   Frederick George Clifford   Alexander Lockie Cockburn   George Thomas Cocket   Edgar Cocks   Frank Cole

William Henry Coleman   Frederick Duncan Coles   Beatrice Cook   Robert Charles Cooke   Albert Smith Stuart Cooper   Edgar Roy Cooper   Clarence Frederick

George Wise Copeland   Walter Henry Copley   John James Coppin   John Cornish   Richard Dennis Cottam   Thomas Luke Coward   David Cowen   Herbert Fisher Cowen

Frederick Richard Bailey Cox   Kenneth Alexander Cragie   Mary Cremin   Albert Oliver Crossland   Sydney Cunninghan   Robert Frank Curry   Cedric Charles Curtis

George Cutting   Edward John Danks   Charles Rees Davies   Henry George Davies   Henry Cecil Davis   James Frederick Davis   Harry Dawson   Elias Dalra Dayee   Alan Daysh

Arthur Dean   Norman Edwin Debenham   Richard Alfred Dickinson   Charles Dobbie   George Dobedoe   George Frederick Dollimore   David Theodore Donald

Charles Edward Donne   Charles Dowding   Frederick Doyle   George Albert Drummond   Charles William Duckett   Thomas Dunlop   Donald Durrant   Edward George Dwyer

Horace Dyer   Minnie Easton   John William Echerman   John Bertram Ecott   Douglas Malcolm Edwards   James Osborne Edwards   Sidney George Edwards

Stanley Arthur Edwards   Walter Espley   Albert Edward Evans   Anthony Falzon   Donald Farrell   Harry Richard Fawn   Arthur George Fenn   Leonard John Robert Finbow

George Cyrill Finch   Wilfred Finlayson   Samuel Fleischmann   James Sutherland Mackay Flett   Albert Henry Foghill   Carmelo Formosa   Norman Forster   Albert Sydney Foxon

Donald Francis   John Franklin   Robert Bonar Fraser   Charles Louis Freeborn   Edward William French   Robert George French   Bert Froggatt   Harry Roy Gammon

Herbert Edward Ganderton   George Gardiner   Albert Henry Garrett   William Charles Gibbons   Ronald George Gibson   William Charles Gilbert   Arthur Charles Gil...

Thomas William Gilling   John Herbert Glasser   Arthur Albert Gould   James Alexander Gow   Arthur Bertram Graham   Dennis Keith Graham   William Graham

Forbes Gran...onas Gray   James Green   Bert Greenfield   Harry Greenwood   Albert Griffiths   Frank Griffiths   Harry Griffiths   Charles Edward Guard   Frederick Henry Habberfield

Leonard Arthur George Hamlyn   John Hanna   Charles Andrew Harding   C.M. Hardman   Leslie Harkin   Frederick John Harris   Thomas Harris   Sydney Harrison

William Arthur Hastings   Roy Haynes   Frank Headland   Charles Healy   Stanley Heard   Harold Dennison Hemings   Joesph Arthur Hemingway

George John Henderson   Robert Henderson   Charles Henry Hennessey   Leonard John Henniker   James Ernest Douglas Henwood   John Herbert   Christopher Hickman

Charles Frederick Higman   William Hill   Arthur James Hillier   Robert James Hills   John Robert Williamson Hobson   W.R. Hodge   Victor Arthur Holderness

Victor Lionel Holloway   Arthur Alexander Holmes   Edward James Holmes   Robert William Holmes   Harold Walter Hook   Alfred George Horrocks

Robert Edward Mark Hotston   James Houlton   Arthur George How   Harry Hoyle   Gordon Edward Huggins   Cecil Leman Ridd Hughes   Eric Heath Hughes   James Hughes

ohn Oliver Hughes   John Ernest Hune   Frederick Walter Hunt   Joel Sarson Hunt   John Caleb Hunt   William Hunter   Joesph Eric Hurding   Jack Huxley   Herbert Cyril Ironside

Edwin Charles Ebenezer Jago   Ernest George Jago   William Edward James-Clarkson   Bertram Frank Jamieson   Thomas Joesph Jamieson   Frank William Jones

Herbert Lewis Jones   Peter Jones   Peter Kenneth Jones   Geoffrey Wallace Jordan   Karl Heinz Kalimann   Maurice John Eustace Keast   George Keefe

Kenneth Evelyn George Keel   Wilfred Leonard Keilly   Francis Kelgy   Denis Trehone Kelly   Walter Joseph George Kempster   Thomas Jefferson Kennedy

ohn William Charles Kenton   Edward Alexander Kenyon   Reginald John Kerby   James Nurse Kerr   Stanley Rowland Kettle   John Christian Kibble   David Killow

Albert Frederick King   Ronald Benjamin King   Charles Edwin Kitto   Rudolph Leopold Kloss   Albert Knight   Reginald Herbert Knowler   George Kyriakides   Douglas Laity

Lionel Molesworth Laity   Herbert Arthur Lamb   Reginald Edward Lansdown   Cyril Lansley   Leonard Thomas Lawrence   Robert Laybourn   Leonard William James Leo...

ohn Nichol Leith   Edwin Reginald Leng   Bernard Herman Lenz   Stanley Lever   Ada Henrietta Levesley   Cecil Sheridan Lewis   Edwin William George Lewin

Robert Henry Lewis   Ronald John Lewis   James Liddle   William Wright Linklater   Kenneth Littlewood   Ronald Locke   Derek Stanley Richard Lowe   Christopher Edward Luga...

Wilfred Lionel Machin   Charles Maguire   Athol Makepeace   Charles Maloney   James Ralph Marklew   Frederick Richard Martin   Leslie Samuel Martin

Dorothy Mason   Frederick Mathers   Harold George Matheson   Charles Albert Mathews   David Charles James Mathews   Lionel Walter Mathews   Arthur Henry May

Maurice Sidney Mayhew   Frederick McCann   Harry McCusker   John McDonald   Thomas Alexander McMurray   Alexander McPhee   Alexander Conning Meach

Arthur John Mendham   Elkan Alexander Mendoza   Thomas Winton Merchant   Arthur Louis Metcalf   Carmelo Micallef   John Micallef   George Edward Middleton

Carmelo Mifsud   Joseph Mifsud   Cecil Miller   Lawrence Victor Miller   Robert Henry Mills   Albert Henry Mitchell   Harry Norman Mitchell   Abraham Shaul Mizrahi

George Joseph Monk   David John Morgan   William Stanley Charles Morgan   Hartley Kirby Morris   Arthur Leonard Morris   Frederick John Morris   James Richard Moun...

Vincent Mula   Joseph Mulligan   Joseph Muscat   Leonard Mynard   Frances Nacey   John Neary   Siegfried Neubauer   Edgar New   Charles Newborn

Frederick Sydney Nicholson   James Niven   Cuthbert Noblett   Joseph Novis   James Frederick Noyce   Michael O Shea   Arthur Robert Oakford   George Organ...

ack Ovenden   Wiliam George Paintin   Charles William Parsons   Walter Reginald Pashley   Gavin Browning Paton   Christopher Railton Patterson

George John Alexander Patterson   Harry Arthur Payne   James Edward Payne   Bertram Henry Peart   Percy Alfred Peletier   Edward Penfold   Cyril Penkethman

Edward Perkins   Ernest Edward Pilgrim   Reginald William Pomfrey   Harold William Poole   Edward Lawrence Potter   Reginald Samuel Charles Francis Potter

Charles William Poulson   Leonard John Powell   Jack George Powney   George Henry Pratt   Thomas James Prestwood   Arthur Geoffrey Prickett   Reginald Prinn

George Frederick Prior   Samuel George Leslie Prior   George Harry Proctor   Lawrence Joseph Proops   Frederick James Puddicombe   Charles Henry Pursey   Ramon Queste...

Arthur George Quirk   John Harry Rands   Ronald Douglas Rawlinson   Arthur James Reed   John Patrick Reed   Sydney Lawrence Bergin Reid   William Maxwell Renne...

William Ribchester   Frank Albert Richards   Jeremiah Richards   Frank Richardson   James Rickerby   Leslie Frank Roberts   Robert Owen Roberts   Lacklan Robertson

Kenneth Herbert   Harold Charles Robinson   James Roche-Kelly   Bertram Sydney Rogers   Philip Eric Rolfe   Walter During Rowe   Leslie William Rowe...

ohn Studen Russ...   Albert Edward Rutter   Cecil John Saunders   George Schembri   Carmelo Sciberras   Charles Scicluna   Charles Herbert Scott   David Sharp

Thomas Cheston Sharp   James Douglas Shearer   Ronald Shrimpton   Charles Arthur Simmonds   Victor Henry Simmonds   John Armstrong Simpson   Robert Sinclai...

Arthur Henry Skerritt   Hugh Skinner   Mervyn John Skinner   Leonard George Hale Sly   Earnest William Smith   Frederick John Smith   Harold George Smith

Leslie Frederick James Smith   Percival Charles Smith   Reginald Clifford Edwin Smith   Richard Stanley Smith   Archibald Smith   Francis Arthur Smith

Frank Douglas Harold Smith   Henry George Stacey   Reginald Stacey   Sydney Stamp   Alfred John Carter Stanley   Roy Albert Henry Staples   George Stark   Reginald Arthur Steed

Ernest Ronald Stevens   Roderick Stewart   Henry William Stilwell   Ian Leonard Stonehouse   Samuel Smith Stothhart   Wilfred William Stretton   Alfred Henry Stubbing...

Albert Sussex   David Sutherland   Cyril Thomas Sutton   Gerald Wiseman Switzer   John Taylor   Walter Henry Edwin Taylor   William John Norton Taylor   William Taylor...

Christopher James Edward Thomas   Albert James Thompson   Albert William Thompson   Herbert William Thompson   Norman Patrick Thompson   Charles Thomson

Howard John Thorpe   Leopold St. John Ticehurst   John Edward Tidd   William Tinsley   George Tiplady   Wilfred Frank Tipper   Jack Titheridge   Edgar Victor Toms

onathan Henry Topham   Hanna Gareabed Toumayan   Joseph Tracey   Albert Edward Traviss   John William Trembath   John Halcrow Trennery   William Treverther...

Cecil John Leonard Tucker   Maud Turner   Ronald Stafford Turner   John Bernard Uffen   Denys John Vaggers   William Vass   Wiliam Louis Vassall...

Charles Edward Vidler   Frederick William Vince   Frederick Horrace Wyman Vizor   Frederick Cyril Wagstaffe   Frederick Charles Walk   Alexander Walke...

Eric Walker   Edgar Patrick Wallace   James Walton   Sarah Lilian Ward   John Tracey Warder   John Albert Ware   Albert Cecil Warwick   Thomas Watson

Alfred Charles Webb   Victor Leslie Webb   Charles Henry Wells   Alfred John West   Harold Leslie West   James Paul Grey Westal...

Lawrence Allan Weston   Christopher Ernest Wheeler   Charles Henry Whincup   Harold John William White   Patrick Godlonton White   Henry Raymond Wigley

Lawrence Thomas Wilkes   William George Wilkins   Frances Wilkinson   Albert Edward Willcock   George Frederick Williams   Jack Arthur William...   Leslie Williams...

Robert Williams   Ronald Willis   Marshall Wilson   Robert Henry Denis Wilson   Richard Windler   Harold Wood   John Wood   Joseph Samuel Ronald Wood

Charles Albert Woods   John Hewitt Worrall   James William Worsfold   Cecil Worth   Norman Wraith   Arthur Cartwright Wright   Duncan McIntosh Yardley   John Alfred Yates

Alfred Kneeshaw Yeadon   Charles James Walton Young   George Young   Louis Charles Septimus Young   Carmelo Zammit   John Zammit   Victor Irving Zann   Lewis Zipser

NAAFI'S PATRON

The practice of members of the Royal Family
lending their names to organisations through
formal patronages is thought to have existed
since the 18th century.

The first recorded patronage was George II's
involvement with the Society of Antiquaries, an
organisation concerned with architectural and
art history, conservation and heraldry. The society
still exists today and retains its Royal patronage
through The Duke of Gloucester's involvement.

NAAFI has also enjoyed a long history of
Royal association since King George VI granted
his patronage to NAAFI in 1946, a link Queen
Elizabeth II continued upon her accession to
the throne in 1952.

*"Please convey my warm thanks to the staff
of The Navy, Army and Air Force Institutes for
their kind message of loyal greetings, sent on
the occasion of NAAFI's Ninetieth Anniversary
which is being celebrated this year.*

*As your patron, I was interested to learn of the
Institute's ongoing work to support Britain's
Armed Forces, as well as the commemorative
events that have been planned for this year. I
much appreciate your thoughtfulness in writing
as you did and, in return, send my best wishes to
all concerned on this most special anniversary."*

Elizabeth R.

CONTENTS

AN INTRODUCTION FROM NAAFI CHIEF EXECUTIVE OFFICER, REG CURTIS

Servitor Servientium; Serving those who Serve.

AS CEO OF THIS UNIQUE AND CHERISHED ORGANISATION IT GIVES ME GREAT PLEASURE TO INTRODUCE THIS COMMEMORATIVE BOOK CELEBRATING 90 YEARS OF NAAFI.

With such a long and distinguished history, there can be few who have not heard of the NAAFI at some stage in their lifetime; indeed I regularly meet people who tell me about how perhaps their parents or other family members have served with NAAFI, and each story is told with warmth and genuine affection for the service we provide.

Unless you have known or worked with NAAFI there are few who fully appreciate the sheer scale of what NAAFI has done over its 90-year existence or indeed the role it continues to play today overseas. Inside this book you will find extraordinary tales of loyalty, devotion and fervour to 'Serving the Services', from our early inception in 1921 right through to our current operations around the world. NAAFI heroes like Tommy Brown, Leslie Calderwood, Major Lynn Cassidy and Captain Thomas Shannon are all mentioned in this book but there are many, many more who have gone above and beyond the call of duty, some of whom paid the ultimate price for their devotion to duty.

Today, although on a much smaller scale, NAAFI staff continue to honour those who have gone before them by providing that vital taste of home in overseas territories such as Afghanistan, Ascension Islands, Brunei, Falklands, Germany, Gibraltar, Northern Ireland and on board Royal Navy Ships. It's their commitment that helps us deliver our service with a smile.

As we celebrate our 90th year 'Serving the Services', I'm sure employees, past and present, would be proud of the work we do today in continuation of that legacy.

I hope you enjoy the book!

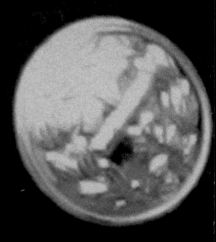

CHIEF OF THE DEFENCE STAFF
GENERAL SIR DAVID RICHARDS
KCB CBE DSO ADC

FOREWORD

THERE MUST BE VERY FEW SERVICE MEN OR WOMEN WHO HAVE NOT HAD SOME CAUSE TO BE DEEPLY GRATEFUL FOR THE EXISTENCE OF THIS REMARKABLE INSTITUTION AT SOME POINT IN THEIR CAREERS.

Whether it be supplying essential services and products to our people in some of the most inhospitable and hostile places on earth, or simply bringing a taste of home to families on the other side of the world, the people of NAAFI have consistently performed their vital role with diligence, dedication and good humour.

From my own time as a young officer in Northern Ireland to most recently as a much older one in Afghanistan, and through many operational and Germany-based tours in between, I have always had nothing but the highest admiration for 'our' NAAFI. The courage and devotion of its people hold a special place in the hearts of the Armed Forces; indeed, they are a critical element in the fabric of our nation's defences.

I would like to take this opportunity to thank the people of NAAFI for the crucial services you provide - we could not be without them. Thank you - and my very best wishes for the next 90 years!

BEFORE NAAFI

The story of NAAFI begins well before 1920.

In 1892, the Hon. Lionel Fortescue, Canteen President of the 17th Lancers, became dissatisfied with the corrupt way in which canteen finances were being handled.

He established a system for keeping a locked till in the canteen and put Sergeant John Gardner in charge, an honest and able man who would later look after hundreds and thousands of pounds as one of the staff of the Navy and Army Canteen Board during World War I.

The locked till practice was soon adopted by other regiments, until another Canteen Officer, Major Harry Crauford of the Grenadier Guards, also dissatisfied with the food provided for his canteen, approached Lionel Fortescue with the idea of forming a co-operative society and doing their own buying. Together, they managed to raise £400 and founded the Canteen and Mess Co-operative Society.

The rule was that interest was not to exceed five per cent, and all further profits were to be handed to the regimental canteen as a rebate. They hoped that in time the co-operative would become a buying and distributing agency for the whole Army.

THE NEED FOR NAAFI GROWS

In August 1914, all arrangements were upset by the outbreak of the Great War.

The Expeditionary Force - the greater part of Britain's regular Army - was sent to France and hundreds of thousands of young men enlisted to fight for King and country.

The Government was unprepared for the problem of supplying and feeding the Forces on a scale never before experienced, so a large Army entered the field without any official provision. Fortunately, the Canteen and Mess Society was still active and was the only contractor which was more concerned with the welfare of the troops than with making money. The Head of the Society was summoned to the War Office together with the Managing Director of Richard Dickenson & Co, the soundest and most experienced firm of the canteen-contractors. The two organisations were invited to establish a special department and subsequently joined together as the Expeditionary Force Canteens to serve the nation.

Even with the extra money and their combined strength, the service could not be increased fast enough to match the huge expansion of the Armed Forces. In the meantime, many new contractors were finding loopholes for exploiting the situation and it became clear that safeguards were needed to protect the interests of the soldiers and supervise the operations of all these vested interests.

In January 1915, a Board of Control was formed and exactly two years later the Army Canteen Committee was registered at the Board of Trade as a company trading not for profit. It absorbed the Canteen and Mess Society, and took over the contracts of Dickenson's and all the other firms supplying the Army in the UK.

Within three months it also took over all canteens abroad where the British troops were stationed during peace times. The Expeditionary Force Canteens were left in charge in the main theatres of war.

In June 1917 the Navy were keen to share in the benefits now being felt by the British soldier and so the Army Canteen Committee assumed the new title of the Navy and Army Canteen Board. When the Royal Air Force became a separate arm of the nation's defences in 1918, their canteens were also absorbed into the Navy and Army Canteen Board.

Lionel Fortescue's vision of a unified canteen system for the Forces was starting to take shape and the nucleus of NAAFI was now in place.

13

NAAFI IS BORN!

After the First World War the Expeditionary Force Canteens (EFC) and the Navy and Army Canteen Board (NACB) did not return to the gratitude of the nation. This was because EFC had made a large amount of profit from the sales of goods to the troops and opinion was divided as to what should be done with the money.

In March 1920 Winston Churchill, then Secretary of State for War, set up a committee to advise on the kind of organisation which would be needed for the Armed Forces in the future. The findings were unanimous; there should be one organisation to serve all three Services, it should be permanent and it should be able to rapidly expand or contract at times of war or peace. The Navy, Army and Air Force Institutes was therefore established on 6th December 1920 and started trading as NAAFI in 1921.

As a not for profit organisation, with no shareholders to reward, NAAFI was asked to run the catering and recreational establishments needed by the Armed Forces. It had to make a profit for the good of NAAFI customers - the men and women in Britain's Armed Forces - and so in addition it undertook to sell goods to servicemen and their families over and above those that were initially provided by the Royal Army Service Corps. The servicemen would benefit directly by getting cash rebates and discounts on purchases and indirectly through surpluses given back as a whole from each year's trading.

For the first time the troops overseas were able to buy the same things in the canteen abroad as they could at home.

NAAFI first saw overseas service in Ireland where British soldiers were sent to deal with a rebellion which followed the granting of independent status to Southern Ireland in 1922. Six years later, NAAFI would have a presence in Bermuda, Ceylon, Germany, Gibraltar, Iraq, Jamaica, China, Malta and the Middle East.

NAAFI RECEIVES ROYAL SEAL OF APPROVAL

At the end of the Great War, the Treaty of Versailles was signed and the coalfields of the Saar Basin were given to France for 15 years.

In 1934 the Saar Plebiscite Force was appointed to act as international peacekeepers in the area. To cater for the British element of the Saar Force, over 40 NAAFI staff travelled to the Saar to provide a canteen shop and service. One NAAFI Manager later wrote:

"We had to improvise very quickly but when the troops arrived a few days later we were ready. By Christmas we were able to supply turkeys, Christmas puddings, mince pies and all the little extras. I don't think many people back home knew what we were doing - or even what NAAFI was."

By the end of December, NAAFI had opened eight combined restaurants and beer bars in Saarbrücken and other large towns, setting up in town halls, a convent, a casino and the hostel of a coalmine. By 1935, NAAFI also provided entertainment with wireless sets, dartboards, ping-pong tables and English daily papers sent over as 'recreational facilities'.

There were other large establishments at Gibraltar, Iraq and Singapore, whilst there were also large NAAFI shore bases at Malta and Aden serving the Headquarters of the important British Mediterranean Fleet, needed to remind the Italian Dictator, Mussolini, not to go too far.

By 1938, the list of countries where NAAFI had staff had grown to include Hong Kong, Shanghai, Egypt, Kenya, Palestine, Transjordan, Sudan, Singapore and Trinidad.

Everywhere it went, NAAFI tried to soften the institutional appearance of the old canteens. Curtains and upholstered chairs took over from trestle tables and hard chairs, whilst clocks, mirrors and framed menus livened up the bare wooden boards. Bright paint kept the NAAFI's clean and smart.

The largest of NAAFI's special catering contracts lasted from 1931 up to the beginning of the Second World War in 1939, by which time the effects of the Wall Street Crash and the American Depression had reached Britain, with serious repercussions for the economy. In light of a rise in bankruptcies and unusually high unemployment, King George V responded to the national crisis with an economy drive; he decided to call in NAAFI to cater for the Household staffs at Buckingham Palace, Windsor Castle, Sandringham, Balmoral and Holyrood House. NAAFI took over the job of buying, preparing and serving food for all grades of the Royal Household, from the servants' hall to the Privy Purse and even the Royal Chef's dining room.

The Royal Palace needed NAAFI; the organisation was able to buy at better prices, streamline the service and half costs. Every Royal occasion called for staff catering; so NAAFI was there at the wedding of Princess Marina to the Duke of Kent in 1934, at the Silver Jubilee of King George V in 1935, at his funeral in 1936 and at the Coronation of King George VI in 1937.

The Jubilee called for an enormous catering effort and NAAFI was up to the challenge. There was a luncheon party at Buckingham Palace for 1,300 members of the Royal Household. In addition, the troops who lined the route and the sailors who filled the streets around Trafalgar Square were also fed by NAAFI, as were the men of the Royal Artillery. Further still, 10,000 special Jubilee teas were served by NAAFI at local celebrations up and down the country.

However, even that effort was surpassed two years later at the Coronation of King George VI. Three enormous canvas canteens were set up in London; two in Kensington Gardens for 1,700 administrative troops and another in Regent's Park for a further 1,500. A further two Messing Stores were also put up to supply up to 31,000 troops during April and May.

On the Tuesday before the Coronation, 33,000 haversack ration packs were prepared, each containing a bread roll, two ounces of wrapped cheese, two apples, one rock cake and two bars of marching chocolate. Meanwhile, over at the Palace, NAAFI served over 17,000 meals to the Royal Household and their guests during Coronation Week.

The final effort was made on the night of 12th May 1937 where 20,000 sausage rolls and rock cakes, 10,000 packets of biscuits and the same number of oranges were issued to all railway stations from which troops were to leave for London. All of this was done in addition to the everyday catering at hundreds of canteens and shops in Britain, and abroad, as well as the steady improvement in the standard of food and comfort for the troops.

In the Far East alone, the list of items which NAAFI bought with its own funds included 11,500 tables, 31,350 chairs, 16,600 armchairs, 3,400 easy chairs, 7,700 pictures, an incredible 30 acres of floor covering and nearly 60 miles of curtaining.

TV PRESENTER & FORCES SWEETHEART
CLAIRE SWEENEY

"*I would like to send my heartfelt congratulations and sincere thanks to all involved in the NAAFI. You guys are fantastic! Having been to several bases around the world and with my brother being in the Army for many years, I'm aware what a great job you do to supply home comforts for our Service men and women and their families. Keep up the good work and congratulations on your 90th year.*"

18

PRELUDE TO WAR AND THE FORMING OF EFI

NAAFI was expected to be able to expand its service on mobilisation. In addition to providing canteens, it would also be responsible for supplying about seventy percent of the soldiers' and airmens' rations at home and large quantities of goods for the Navy. When war broke out, NAAFI would have to organise the same thing for the Territorial Army and the entirely new transcript Armies.

When war finally came no-one could have predicted the needs and complexities of all that would be required. Although NAAFI had been the 'fourth arm' of the fighting services, the organisation was civilian in character. In Britain, staff could continue to be civilians and serve the troops, but once overseas, staff would be operating in theatres of war where discipline had to be immediate and unqualified. If taken prisoner, NAAFI staff had to have the same safeguards as soldiers under the Geneva Convention.

To get round this, the Expeditionary Force Institutes (EFI) were formed and wore the uniform of the Royal Army Service Corps. The staff serving on HM ships and at shore establishments overseas as part of the Naval Canteen Service (NCS), also wore naval uniform, although they weren't officially enrolled into the Royal Navy until 1942.

Although some of NAAFI's EFI officers had served in the First World War, the majority went out in the early days with little more than their uniform and their courage. Men who came in knowing no-one more daunting than an awkward customer, left as trained soldiers ready to lend armed support to those in the front line.

However, in spite of this, NAAFI, through EFI, still had an advanced party in France two days after the British Expeditionary Force landed on 4th September. On many occasions NAAFI would even be ahead of the Army, and in Naples in 1943, NAAFI had a meal prepared and ready for the advancing troops when they entered the city.

After the war the Daily Mail wrote: "Morale is one of the most powerful of armaments" when it referred to NAAFI as one of the three institutions that kept the nation going.

BRITAIN AT WAR!

Between 1939 and 1945 NAAFI's star had never been brighter.

In 1939 Britain was at war with Germany for the second time in a generation. However, for the first time in history a British Army was taking a fully equipped and organised canteen service. The number of NAAFI employees would rise from 8,000 to a peak of 110,000 and its trading establishments from 1,300 to nearly 10,000, including 900 mobile canteens and a further 800 on ships.

War was declared on Sunday 3rd September, and as usual, NAAFI was quick off the mark. The day before, 500 NAAFI staff in the UK received red envelopes marked as 'priority' and by 2pm on Sunday they were on their way to Territorial Army drill halls for medical examination and attestation. By Friday of that week, all 500 enlisted men had been equipped and given 48 hours leave.

On Tuesday 12th September, 250 NAAFI staff left Kensington for France and arrived early the next morning with a second party arriving two days later. Together they set up depots at Brest and Nantes, four Bulk Issue Stores and canteen accommodation for 41,000 soldiers and airmen.

By May 1940, NAAFI were responsible for looking after an Army of 1.75 million troops at home and around 800,000 overseas.

COMIC, ACTOR AND FOUNDING MEMBER OF THE GOONS
MICHAEL BENTINE CBE

"

"Like so many of my 'cannon fodder' generation, I experienced much of the worst of the war. As a very junior Anglo-Peruvian photo-journalist, working in Fleet Street while I was earnestly trying to join the RAF, I went through practically all of the 1940/41 bombing of London.

After each night of hideous destruction, one of the first vehicles to trundle its rattling way through the smoking shambles would be a NAAFI canteen truck, one of many sent in from the nearest Service units. Whenever it stopped and opened up its side panel to reveal the serving counter, a queue of exhausted men and women, both Service and civilian, quickly formed. Within minutes everyone gratefully clutched a mug of that wonderfully comforting, steaming hot, sweet, dark brown brew of 'corpse reviving' NAAFI tea! Squatting down on the nearest pile of rubble, we sank our teeth into those other delights, NAAFI 'Wads'! These were large, life-sustaining 'Rock Cakes' made of off-white wartime flour, sugar and bicarbonate of soda, well browned on the outside, dotted with

scorched currants and somehow reminiscent of the Rock of Gibraltar and all that it stood for! Yet, to those of us who had been helping the National Fire Service to fight the terrifying fires, or for those poor devils who had been bombed out by the terror raids, this thrice welcome snack was Nector and Ambrosia, the food of the Gods!

The reason I have had this long-standing love affair with NAAFI is that, no matter how grim the situation, in air raids, during long-range shelling across the English Channel, or being under heavy fire in Europe, somehow, somewhere, those welcome NAAFI trucks and their cheerful crews were always there, no matter what the cost some of them paid in death, pain and suffering. The simple friendly cheer they brought with them was truly a slice of sanity in a world gone mad. God bless them. Every one!"

Quoted in 1996 at the time of NAAFI's 75th Anniversary

IN EARLY 1940, GEORGE DAKIN
FOUND HIMSELF TRANSFORMED
FROM A MIDLANDS GROCER TO A
NAVAL CANTEEN SERVICE MANAGER.
HE SERVED ON DESTROYERS, FIRSTLY
ON HMS HIGHLANDER DURING THE
D-DAY LANDINGS IN AND LATER IN
THE EVACUATION OF NORWAY.

GEORGE DAKIN

"All NAAFI personnel were an integral part of the ship's company. For example, during the rescue work following the sinking of the Lancastria, I was supplying 4.7 inch shells to the forward gun. We were under air attack from the Germans the whole time! Meanwhile, my colleague Frank Clements was helping to pull in survivors from the sea which was covered with a film of oil. We both helped to wash the oil and fuel from their bodies and then helped transfer them to the troopship Oronsay which took them back home to Plymouth. Frank took the only published pictures of the sinking of the Lancastria.

At the same time I was also running the canteen which was responsible for much of the feeding of the ships' company. The canteen supplied eggs, bacon, sausages, liver, fish, cheese, pork and other items and it was usual to prepare quite a variety of food every day. One mess might have kippers for breakfast, another sausages, another bacon and eggs! When I was on the Volunteer, I was expected to get a leg of pork for each Mess for Sunday dinner; it made a lot of difference to the morale of the ships' company.

During 'Operation Vigorous' from Alexandria to Malta, a torpedo blew a great hole right through our bows and we were listed for repairs at Brooklyn Naval Dockyard in New York. I was always the first ashore to buy fresh fruit and other canteen necessities and when we got to New York I loaded up with canned fruit and meat, chocolate and biscuits so that every sailor had presents to take back home when he arrived in England for Christmas."

A few days after getting married in 1941, George's friend, Frank Clements left for the Far East as NAAFI Manager on-board HMS Exeter. The ship was sunk by the Japanese in the Java Sea on his first wedding anniversary and he became a Japanese Prisoner of War for 1,264 days in grim conditions at Makassor. During all of that time his wife had no news of his whereabouts until he finally arrived home in December 1945.

NAAFI UNDER FIRE

NAAFI personnel came under fire very early on in the war. Exactly 14 days after war was declared NAAFI suffered its first casualties when NCS canteen staff W.H. Copley, E.G. Bishop, A.G. Matheson, A.G. Quirk and E.P. Wallace were killed on-board HMS Courageous when it was torpedoed by a German submarine. By the spring of 1940, five other Canteen Managers and a Trainee Manager serving on-board HMS Daring, HMS Exmouth, HMS Grenville and HMS Sphinx had also lost their lives through enemy action.

In June 1940, St Nazaire at the mouth of the River Loire was crowded with troops and airmen who had retreated from the areas west of the River Seine. That night, the Germans made a number of heavy attacks on the town and docks below and the following morning a large number of NAAFI staff made their way through the rubble to the quayside whilst still under attack. It was five days before France finally fell and the largest ship at anchor in Quiberon Bay was the SS Lancastria. During the morning, she took troops on board until every foot of her decks, holds and cabins were filled - over 6,000 men, including 400 of the NAAFI staff.

At 2.15pm the Lancastria was given permission to leave but her Commander decided to wait in the hope of getting an escort across the U-boat infested Channel. It proved to be a fatal decision. At 3.50pm, seven JU87s and Dorniers scored four direct hits, exploding in the engine room and blowing open the Lancastria's hull. At 4.18pm, barely 30 minutes after the ship had received its final hit, she sank taking 3,000 lives, 300 of whom were from NAAFI.

The fall of France, the evacuation of Dunkirk and the sinking of the Lancastria meant that in addition to the tragic human loss, NAAFI lost over a million pounds worth of goods. After Dunkirk and with the troops back in England, much had to be done quickly to feed and house them. NAAFI's home service had to expand to cater not only for the Garrisons in Britain but also for the troops on leave and in transit.

Seven months after Dunkirk, the number of canteens in Britain had doubled to 3,600 and by June 1942, the number had tripled. NAAFI opened bakeries and sausage factories and became self-sufficient in providing hearty British family meals such as meat and potato rolls, sausage and mash and fish and chips. However, NAAFI was also expected to cater for the thousands of soldiers, sailors and airmen from the Commonwealth and Allied countries under German occupation. To ensure they all had their traditional dishes, NAAFI also produced curries and chapatis for the Indians, sour herrings and minced fish for the Norwegians, dumplings and beetroot soup for the Poles, peanut butter and maple syrup for the Canadians and Jonnycake and pumpkin pie for the Americans!

DOUBLE OLYMPIC CHAMPION
DAME KELLY HOLMES DBE MBE

"

"Having joined the Army at the age of 18, you need a place to relax and meet with your colleagues at the end of a long, hard day - I did this regularly during my career in the Army. The role of NAAFI is often misunderstood and rarely praised, but just reading some of the stories in this book is testament to the great job you have done, and continue to do, in supporting our brave men and women around the world. I'm proud to have served in the British Army and it's nice to be able to show my appreciation for NAAFI in this commemorative book. I wish you all the very best in your 90th year."

WAR IN THE MEDITERRANEAN

After the Battle of Britain, the central focus of the war shifted to the Mediterranean.

Gibraltar was in danger of invasion by Spain. Italy had invaded Greece but was struggling to fight off the Greek Army so Germany marched through Yugoslavia to support the Italians. Heavily outnumbered, the British and Allied troops were forced to evacuate southern Greece, enlisting the Royal Navy's assistance to transport them to Crete.

In May 1941, the Germans launched a parachute invasion of Crete. During the 10-day battle for the islands, Captain Thomas Shannon, a veteran of the First World War and in charge of NAAFI on Crete, was wounded and captured by the Nazis, taken to Greece and held in a camp outside Salonika. It was there that he organised the escapes of 42 Allied soldiers, until he was discovered and sent to a POW camp in Germany. In November 1943, he escaped himself and returned to England via Sweden before returning to duty in the Middle East. For his gallantry he was awarded the Military Cross.

Two NAAFI Sergeants in Crete also won lasting renown. Sergeant Edwin Pratt and Sergeant Leslie Calderwood were also taken prisoner by the Germans and escaped, this time to live with the Cretan peasants in the mountains. After nine months 'Ted' Pratt escaped to Egypt with Leslie Calderwood choosing to stay and fight with the Partisans. The latter was later awarded both the Military Medal and the NAAFI Gallantry Award.

"As an 18-year-old National Serviceman the NAAFI offered a refuge from the rigours of the parade ground and the seemingly endless 'bull'. The thought of a cuppa and a wad of fruit cake after a morning's drill or weapon training certainly helped things along. I can remember sitting around nattering about everything under the sun - and there were sing-songs, usually with a Scouse on the piano - and of course there were the 'NAAFI Girls' to talk to! What more could a squaddie want?

I think the most memorable NAAFI of all the ones I had known in Aldershot, Egypt and Germany was the building in Peninsular Barracks, Haifa. It was a long wooden hut with a veranda facing the beach and I never even had a cup of tea there!

The 3rd Para Battalion had just moved in. I think it was early December 1947 and I'd been picked for guard duty on our first night there. About 4.30 in the morning I was walking down to the cookhouse to get a bucket of tea and there was this red glow in the sky and I thought how pretty it was. Sunrise on the Med.

Now I should explain that the NAAFI was next to a couple of huts which housed the Battalion Armoury - full of mortar bombs, Piat bombs, grenades, 9mm and .303 ammo - and the cookhouse was just across the road about 30 yards away. The red glow turned out to be the blazing NAAFI and Armoury!

There were paras all over the place shifting the ammo out of the blazing huts and stacking it across the road, next to the cookhouse! The RSM was there in pyjama trousers and vest plus 9mm pistol. The lads were naked or in PT shorts - all sorts of undress. I was told to drop the tea bucket and get in and help shift the boxes of bombs. We were doing this as fast as we could when somebody shouted "the ceiling's on fire". That was it. We all got out of there and ran in all directions! A minute or so later there was an almighty bang as the stuff we'd stacked outside the cookhouse went the same way! So that was the end of the armoury, the cookhouse and the NAAFI.

A strange sequel to this episode occurred when I was filming in Israel in 1964. Our Israeli Assistant and I were chatting about the fact that I'd been to Israel in '61 with another film and mentioned that I'd been in Haifa with the Paras in '47/'48. He said that he too was in Haifa at that time. He was 16-years-old and with the Haganah and he had been part of the team that had fired on the NAAFI and caused the Armoury to explode!

All my best wishes to NAAFI in their 90th year, keep up the great work you do in serving Her Majesties Forces; here's to another 90 years!"

THE WESTERN DESERT

The contribution made by NAAFI to the changing fortunes of the war in the Western Desert was remarkable, with staging areas set up at 100 mile intervals westwards from Alexandria. Supplies came by the single line railway or by sea into the tiny ports in Egypt and Libya and were dumped on the sand, with only a barbed wire fence to deter looters. Egypt was then a British stronghold on which the Allies depended for their grip on North Africa and the Middle East and it became NAAFI's largest overseas base.

As the tide of the war turned, tented camps were replaced by more permanent buildings which were taken over as breweries and bakeries. It was during the campaign in north-west Africa that NAAFI began to include social amenities for the men and women as well as meals, refreshments and shopping. NAAFI had always run clubs for the Officers, but now opened its clubs to all ranks where a man could get a bath and a shave, read the newspaper, play billiards or even watch a film.

The most spectacular NAAFI Club set up later in the war was in Italy in June 1944. It was housed in Prince Umberto's Palace in Naples, home to the rulers of Naples and Sicily for three hundred years. Described as the 'finest soldiers club in the world' there was an art gallery, a gymnasium and a room where 1,300 could dine at a sitting.

NAAFI helped to bring life back to Italy. They restored Opera Houses, hotels and restaurants and many of Italy's breweries today owe their origins to the brew masters released from the British and Italian Armies at that time.

NAAFI GIRLS

The NAAFI girls proved their sterling worth throughout the war.

In 1939 around half of the staff were women and by the middle of the war there were over 60,000 employed. They peeled potatoes, scrubbed floors and cooked meals for the hungry servicemen at a moment's notice, but above all, they kept their nerve and sense of humour under every kind of hardship and bombardment. Inevitably there were complaints - of drab premises, shortages of cigarettes - but in spite of the uncomfortable and often basic conditions, the NAAFI girls endeavoured to make up with friendship and comfort for what was lacking in their surroundings. One Army Sergeant said of them: *"We'd have paid them for their smile if they hadn't had any beer. You can't know what it meant to come back out from the desert and see a lass from home"*.

Often the only British girls in the Command, NAAFI girls were overwhelmed with invitations for their off-duty hours. So much were they in demand that a system was introduced to where anyone wishing to take out a NAAFI girl for the evening had to sign a receipt and give an undertaking to return her to her quarters at a certain time.

FORCES SWEETHEART AND TV PRESENTER
LORRAINE KELLY

"

"NAAFI and in particular the 'NAAFI Girls' have always had a special place within Armed Forces life. Our Service men and women serve our country with loyalty, bravery and professionalism in some of the most hostile and inhospitable areas in the world and so to have NAAFI there alongside them, offering them an escape from all that, is just fantastic. Whether it is a cup of NAAFI tea, a chocolate bar or a comforting and reassuring chat, you all do a great job and I'm delighted to offer my congratulations and best wishes to all of you on your 90th year. Long may it continue!"

31

D-DAY

On 6th June 1944, NAAFI's years of experience in North Africa and then Italy were used in the greatest sea and airborne landings ever known.

On the Normandy beaches over half a million troops landed in little over a week and by the end of August over two million men were moving eastwards. In the weeks before D-Day, troops had moved south and NAAFI moved with them, closing down their canteens in the north to provide organised parties, games and competitions at each of the larger centres. The atmosphere was tense which meant relaxation was vital to keep spirits and morale high.

In May 1944 NAAFI's warehouses in England were overflowing, with shipments of a thousand tons a week scheduled to go across the Channel after the landings. Canteens could not be opened until a bridgehead had been established so NAAFI packs were issued to every soldier involved in the invasion.

NAAFI was supposed to be in operation in Normandy 30 days after D-Day, yet despite the gales and storms, NAAFI opened its first base canteen at Sully on 1st July, well ahead of time.

Two weeks later there were two base canteens, eight stores and two mobile canteens. On route, one of the mobile canteens lost its

way and entered the Belgian town of St. Vincent ahead of the forward troops. It was taken to be an armoured car of the resistance and six Allied airmen hiding in a cellar were liberated! The other mobile canteen had a similarly strange experience when it received the surrender of German soldiers and promptly delivered them to a POW camp along with the provisions!

Each NAAFI pack contained cigarettes, tobacco, matches, toothpaste, shaving soap, razor blades, cubes of meat extract, cocoa, milk tablets, chewing gum, letter cards and pencils.

NAAFI TEA AND THE FAMOUS 'NAAFI BREAK'

Since the early 1920s, NAAFI has produced the tea that keeps our men and women fighting fit on front line operations. The famous 'cup of char and wad of cake' was sold from mobile vans in the streets of London during the blitz, in Berlin in 1945 and in the desert during Operation Desert Storm.

In September 1939 the Empire Tea Board revolutionised the Army's tea making and 'the best tea the Army ever tasted' was served on the beaches of Dunkirk - 2,000 cups on the first day of the evacuation, 62,000 on the second day and by the end, 330,000 troops had been served from the canteens. In 1944, 14 million cups of tea were being served by NAAFI every day!

The arrival of an admin/tea break has long been linked with taking a 'NAAFI Break' and, even in countries where NAAFI no longer has a presence, the phrase is still commonly used.

In the context of Forces life, a 'NAAFI Break' was so much more than a tea break; it was a chance to unwind, catch up with friends or take a glance at the daily newspaper. It was a real heart-warming taste of home as well as being a morale-boosting link to normality.

The liquid lifeline which became synonymous with NAAFI during wartime is still the Forces favourite today and was re-launched to the UK public in 2010 to mark NAAFI's 90th year.

Image courtesy of the Council of the National Army Museum, London.

ENSA

One Sunday morning in the summer of 1938, four theatre men - Basil Dean, Owen Nares, Godfrey Tearle and Leslie Henson - asked the question: *"What will the theatre do if there is a Second World War?"* They wanted to stir the world of theatre, concert hall and cinema into action for what was to come. The result was the Entertainments National Service Association (ENSA) - the entertainments branch of NAAFI.

ENSA would be responsible for recruiting the performers and for the theatrical organisation. On 11th September, Drury Lane Theatre was taken over by NAAFI as the headquarters of the entertainments branch for the exclusive use of ENSA, as professional entertainment came to sit comfortably alongside the provision of food and comfort for the troops.

Soon there was a steady stream of recruits. Only three weeks after war was declared, the first 15 concert parties, made up of over 100 artistes plus wardrobes, travelling stages and transport were assembled on the Drury Lane stage ready to go. It was a remarkable achievement by even NAAFI's standards.

The first ENSA concert in France had Gracie Fields as the star. Few who remember the BBC broadcast of that concert will forget the sound of the soldiers belting out the choruses of 'Sally' and every soldiers' mother back home imagined their son's voice was among them.

By 1944 there were over 4,000 artistes on the NAAFI payroll and in one month ENSA put on over 13,500 stage shows and 20,000 films in every theatre of war, as well as to workers in munitions factories and in remote areas in the Faroes, Orkneys, Iceland, Madagascar and the Azores.

What ENSA meant to the men and women who were living and fighting in gruelling, dangerous and sometimes horrifying conditions is difficult to encapsulate, but few have described it better than the actor Dirk Bogarde who wrote: *"It was the darkest, coldest, cruellest winter just after the disaster of Arnhem. My Division never quite made it to Arnhem but stayed bogged down in mud and despair just across the river, watching in helpless frustration the hideous death of a dream, a city and much of its population. Uselessly one wept, or dragged muddied, bloodied, soaking bodies up the slithering banks and watched as our youth (I was 23) drained away into the swirling waters of the Rhine."*

Summoned to HQ in Eindhoven he went on: *"To my amazement I saw a poster stuck on a tree which announced that ENSA, the highly abused Entertainment for the troops, had finally reached us. That night and for seven nights, we were to see The Merry Widow at the giant Phillips Works Theatre; the stars were to be Madge Elliot and Cyril Ritchard, two elderly but gallant stars from the real West End Stage. I was among the first in the queue. I sat enraptured in my seat as the orchestra crashed into the overture with mittened hands and sheer glory, magic, beauty, life and fun was set before us. I went to every performance. Because of The Merry Widow and its frothy nonsense which they and their gallant company brought us in the darkest of winters in the saddest of places, I swear that hundreds of us took heart and survived."*

Thousands of famous stars gave performances for nominal fees under the ENSA banner, including Dame Vera Lynn, Will Fyffe, George Robey, George Formby, Arthur Askey, Flanagan and Allen, Beatrice Lilley, Josephine Baker, Vivien Leigh, Richard Tauber, Geraldo, Benno Moiseiwitch and Sir Adrian Boult.

COURAGE OVER AND ABOVE THE LINE OF DUTY

From the beginning of hostilities until 1946, over 550 NAAFI staff lost their lives on active service.

They fell in the Far East, in Greece, in the Western Desert and Italy, in France and in Germany. Some went down with ships of the Royal Navy whilst others died in canteens at home when the bombs came down. One hundred and fifty of these men and women were decorated for courage and mentioned in dispatches.

Perhaps NAAFI's most famous son was the 16-year-old NAAFI Canteen Assistant on-board HMS Petard who helped retrieve vital German 'Enigma' codes during the Second World War. Today, the late Tommy Brown from North Shields, remains the youngest ever recipient of the George Medal.

The names of these heroic individuals are remembered in a hand written Roll of Honour which is given pride of place at The Garrison Church of St George, Bulford Camp, Wiltshire.

IN 1941, ANXIOUS TO DO HIS BIT FOR HIS COUNTRY, 15-YEAR-OLD TOMMY BROWN FROM NORTH SHIELDS LIED ABOUT HIS AGE AND MANAGED TO TALK HIS WAY INTO A JOB WITH NAAFI. WITHIN A YEAR TOMMY WAS ON ACTIVE SERVICE AS A CANTEEN ASSISTANT ABOARD HMS PETARD, A DESTROYER DESTINED TO BECOME PART OF A REMARKABLE STORY THAT WOULD CHANGE THE COURSE OF THE SECOND WORLD WAR.

TOMMY BROWN GM

On 30th October 1942, HMS Petard was in waters off Port Said on the Egyptian coast investigating reports of radar contact with a German submarine, later identified as U-559 due to its distinctive white donkey emblem on the conning tower. A sustained depth charge attack was laid down, eventually forcing the U-boat to the surface, and after Petard's 4-inch guns caused serious damage, the crew started to abandon ship.

Quick action was needed if the submarine was to give up any secrets. First Lieutenant Tony Fasson together with Able Seaman Colin Grazier dived into the sea and swam across to the stricken vessel. They were closely followed in one of Petard's boats by NAAFI Canteen Assistant Tommy Brown who was now 16-years-old. Clambering down into U-559 the two navy men made their way to the captain's cabin where they found two code books, a Short Weather Cipher and Short Signal Book. Passing them out to Tommy they went back into the submarine to continue their search before Tommy shouted a warning to get out. As they started up the ladder, U-559 made her final dive taking Tony Fasson and Colin Grazier with her. They would never know the importance of their actions and nor, thanks to the cloak of secrecy that was thrown around the incident, would anyone else for a very long time.

These were desperate times for convoys braving U-boat packs in the Atlantic as had Germany managed to prevent merchant ships from carrying food, raw materials, and troops from North America to Britain, the outcome of the Second World War could have been very different. It took 24 days to get the code books from U-559 to Bletchley Park in Buckinghamshire, where Britain's top code breakers struggled for months to crack the code of the upgraded M4 Enigma Triton, after the Germans introduced a fourth rotor into their brilliant Enigma machine code systems.

Thankfully, the breakthrough came on December 13th 1942 when the cryptanalysts learned that the four-letter indicators for regular U-boat messages were the same as those for the three-letter indicators with the addition of one further letter. This meant that once a daily key was found for a weather message the four-rotor signals needed to be tested in only 26 positions to find the full key. Only an hour after the first decrypts were made intercepts of U-boat signals were sent to the Admiralty's submarine tracking room, revealing the positions of 15 submarines! For the first time in a long time, U-boat movements were exposed and the use of long-range bombers and anti-submarine tactics gradually turned the tide in Britain's favour.

Both Fasson and Grazier were awarded the George Cross and Tommy Brown, the 16-year-old NAAFI Canteen Assistant from North Shields, received the George Medal. Unfortunately for Tommy, his courage that night led to an unexpected turn of events. With all the attention he received, his age became known to the authorities costing him his posting and resulting in an unwanted return home to Tyneside. His courage that night will never be forgotten, something that was to be proved again in 1945 when, tragically, he lost his life trying to rescue his sister from a house fire.

VICTORY!

While Europe was celebrating victory, the war was not over yet. With an extraordinary grasp of military strategy, NAAFI had foreseen the need for the British Fleet to operate in the Pacific and supplying this Fleet would prove to be one of the greatest challenges of the war.

In spite of dock strikes and shortages of boats and equipment, NAAFI's Naval Canteen Service overcame every obstacle. Landing crafts full of men and stores were ready to sail when the bombs at Hiroshima and Nagasaki brought the war to an abrupt end.

MV Menestheus - or the floating pub as it became known - was unique among 'ships taken from the trade' and used by the Navy in times of conflict.

Originally built in 1929 for Holt's Blue Funnel Line, the ship was taken over by the Admiralty and fitted as a minelayer ten years later, before work began in 1944 to convert her into an 'Amenities' ship, designed to provide the troops on shore and afloat with leisure facilities.

It was the on-board brewery, however, that set the Menestheus apart from other logistics ships. For the first and only time in the Navy's history, beer was brewed afloat and served in surroundings furnished by Hamptons and Maples. It was the closest thing to a country club afloat. There was a cinema, fully equipped theatre, sports facilities for boxing and water polo, a library, chapel, a tailors shop, barber and a laundrette amongst other things.

Unfortunately, by the time Menestheus was refitted, the war was over and the British Pacific Fleet had a permanent base once again in Hong Kong. She eventually left the Pacific in 1946 and arrived home two months later when, like Cinderella leaving the ball, her fine robes were stripped away and she returned to her former service.

NAAFI's service to the Armed Forces had not cost the country a penny. Not only that, it had also given surplus profits to the Benevolent and Welfare funds of the Services - a unique role of NAAFI that still continues to this day.

FIRST SEA LORD AND CHIEF OF NAVAL STAFF
ADMIRAL SIR MARK STANHOPE GCB OBE ADC

"D'YOU HEAR THERE? THE NAAFI CANTEEN WILL BE OPEN FOR THE NEXT THREE-ZERO MINUTES."

That main broadcast pipe on-board a warship is invariably the cue for sailors from all over the ship to converge on the NAAFI, where the day's events, jokes and gossip will be shared while queuing for the range of goods on offer. On-board HM ships, the NAAFI staff are completely integrated members of the ship's company, and a very welcome addition. They bring a different perspective, very often a range of skills beyond their catering management role, and of course, through their product range, reminders of home for sailors who will have been deployed away for many months. They have also fought alongside their ship's companies, and died with them in times of war. From the iconic bravery of 16-year-old canteen assistant Tommy Brown GM, through the hundreds of NAAFI staff who gave their lives in World War Two, to those who fought in the Falklands and Gulf Wars, the link between the Naval Service and the NAAFI has always been particularly close.

To this day, wherever you find our ships, deployed globally across the world, or in Afghanistan where NAAFI staff support our Royal Marines, those links with the Naval Service remain just as strong.

I am delighted to add my support to the celebrations marking the 90th anniversary of The Navy, Army and Air Force Institutes, and congratulate all the men and women of NAAFI, past and present, who have given - and continue to give - such valued support to our Armed Forces.

WAR IS OVER - WHAT NOW?

If peace in 1945 brought relief and freedom to the returning troops, it also brought about a number of problems for NAAFI. In 1939-40, the main problem had been how to expand; now it was how to shrink without collapsing.

On the day after VE-Day, the Commander of the Fleet in Scapa Flow told NAAFI's Area Manager that he could leave, resulting in the entire Fleet sailing for Australian waters. Deprived of all their customers at a stroke, Area Managers closed canteens almost daily. In the months following VE-Day, the whole of northern Europe was a disaster area and food was in chronically short supply. Without NAAFI canteens and ration packs, the majority of troops returning home would have gone hungry, and whilst canteens closed in France and Italy, others opened in occupied Germany.

During the years following the end of the war, there was hardly a month went by when Britain's Armed Forces were not under attack or keeping the peace somewhere in the world. In those post-war years NAAFI had to dispose of huge amounts of stock in places where they had suddenly been ordered to move. By the end of 1947, 110,000 staff had been halved and by 1955 halved again.

NAAFI was catering for thousands in West Berlin when the Russians imposed their blockade in 1948. For several months, staff existed only on the supplies they already had, often no more than tinned food and dried potatoes. The blockade was broken by an airlift of goods carried by British and American aircraft over the Russian zone to the beleaguered city, with NAAFI staff at Wünsdorf working 24 hours a day loading old wartime bombers and transport aircraft with supplies. A NAAFI mobile was the very first of a convoy of vehicles to enter Berlin when the blockade was lifted, and no vehicle was more welcome.

CHANGE IN THE AIR: PEACE AND WAR

There were many important changes for NAAFI in the 1950s as living standards and the expectation of higher quality goods and services was growing fast. Although better paid, there were fewer soldiers and a higher proportion of families in the Services.

Out went the old image of the NAAFI canteen with the wooden floors and table tops pockmarked with carved initials and in came clubs, each individual in design and décor for comfort. Restaurants, bars, television and games rooms began to appear and old-fashioned cookers were replaced with modern infrared grills and electric griddles. Steak and chips replaced baked beans on toast as the most popular meal.

The goods stocked by NAAFI also grew enormously, varying from cigarette lighters and watches, to washing machines and record players. The work of the Supplies Department included both the supply of messing goods to units and the Special Catering Department which handled functions from unit parties, to the Coronation of Queen Elizabeth II in 1953.

TV CELEBRITY CHEF
JAMES MARTIN

"*I'm delighted to offer my best wishes and congratulations to all of you at NAAFI during your 90th year. For people like me, who don't come from a Forces background, many haven't even heard of NAAFI never mind know what its role is within the British Forces. During my recent visit to you in Germany, it was amazing to see just what a great job you do to provide that British environment overseas - bars, clubs and stores provide everything you would need from fresh groceries and daily newspapers, to sound systems and even car sales! It really is unbelievable. You're all doing a great job in supporting our Service men and women overseas and I wish you all the very best for the future.*"

THE ELIZABETHAN ERA BEGINS

In February 1952 Queen Elizabeth II followed her father, King George VI, by granting her patronage to NAAFI. This set the seal on a link which began in 1946 when His Royal Highness became NAAFI's first Patron.

A year later, NAAFI had become so vital to the Armed Forces that it became part of every expedition. For a few months during 1953, staff had the unique experience of setting up a shop on a desert island in support of the team which was to test Britain's first atomic weapon. A small bay on one of the otherwise uninhabited Monte Bello Islands was netted to provide a shark-free swimming pool with a canteen alongside.

Islands were a familiar part of the NAAFI scene in the 1950s. The last was the tiny outpost of Gan, 600 miles south west of Ceylon which was leased from the Maldive Islands as an RAF staging post. Before the British Forces took over the island, the local population had been undernourished, living only on their fishing catch. However, the RAF and NAAFI offered them work building the base and with good pay, spent in the NAAFI shop, their health improved enormously.

The island of Gan at that time provided a snapshot of how far NAAFI had already come from the basic canteen facilities of the early 1920s. It had become the universal provider, not only for the Forces, but for local staff as well. In addition to the cooking and running canteens, NAAFI also provided the hairdresser, the cobbler, the tailor and the baker.

As troops began to enjoy the benefits of better pay, the European Canteen Service was formed in 1955 to reflect the changing relationship between Germany and the foreign forces on her soil. It proved to be a watershed in Anglo-German relations; the old enemy was now an equal partner in NATO.

The Allied Forces in Egypt were responsible for the security of an area stretching as far south as Somaliland and East Africa, north to Greece, east to Iran and west to Libya, when the Suez crisis of 1956 threatened to send the world to war. Around 700 Service families were moved from Cairo and Alexandria into specially built communal villages, as Egypt suddenly became impatient for independence. In the process, NAAFI staff had to move £2.5m worth of stock from 14 warehouses and close 250 clubs and canteens in the delta amidst a hostile local population. NAAFI was now pulling out of Iraq and Syria, where 40 canteens had been built but were never opened because of the sudden reversal of military plans.

On one occasion, NAAFI had a surplus stock of tins of syrup and herrings and gave them to their employees; no-one thought to explain how such unfamiliar delicacies should be eaten. The Maldiveans produced a unique recipe where the centre was scooped out of a loaf of bread and filled with herrings and syrup. It was eaten with relish and the dish survives in Gan to this day!

CHIEF OF THE AIR STAFF
AIR CHIEF MARSHAL SIR STEPHEN DALTON
KCB ADC BSC FRAES CCMI RAF

SINCE ITS FORMATION IN DECEMBER 1920, THE NAVY, ARMY AND AIR FORCE INSTITUTES HAS SUPPORTED THE ROYAL AIR FORCE ACROSS THE GLOBE. DURING THOSE PAST 90 YEARS NAAFI HAS SERVED ALONGSIDE THE MILITARY IN ALMOST EVERY THEATRE INCLUDING THE FALKLANDS, BELIZE, CYPRUS, BOSNIA, GERMANY, IRAQ AND AFGHANISTAN.

NAAFI means many different things to different people. During the Second World War and its aftermath, veterans will remember fondly the NAAFI wagons and clubhouses which provided food and relaxation in often very difficult circumstances. For those serving in the Royal Air Force from the seventies through to the nineties, most memories will be of the relatively good life in post-war Germany where bases such as Laarbrüch, Brüggen, Gatow and Gütersloh were served by modern NAAFI supermarkets or department stores and well-founded leisure facilities providing a taste of home as well as the opportunity for employment for many Service family members. More recently, NAAFI has worked in extremely challenging environments in Bosnia and Iraq and has deployed more than 90 civilian and uniformed staff (Expeditionary Forces Institute) to Afghanistan to provide very welcome recreational facilities, working and living alongside Service personnel and sharing their often dangerous and difficult working conditions.

The biggest challenge for NAAFI over the past 90 years has been adapting to changing force structures and locations, which has required it to rapidly expand and contract in times of war and peace. In an uncertain world, these challenges are unlikely to diminish and I applaud the way in which the NAAFI management and staff have risen to these challenges with good humour whilst striving to maintain a high standard of service.

I am proud to support your 90th anniversary celebrations and congratulate every member of the NAAFI, both past and present, who have given such excellent support to the Royal Air Force.

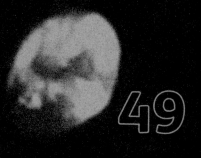

EVELINE WINKMANN RETIRED IN DECEMBER 2008 HAVING WORKED FOR NAAFI SINCE 1963. BEFORE RETIREMENT EVELINE WORKED IN THE PROPERTY DEPARTMENT BUT, AS SHE FONDLY REMEMBERS, THIS WAS A LONG WAY FROM WHERE SHE STARTED OUT.

EVELINE WINKMANN

"I first joined NAAFI on 22nd April 1963 when I was just 17-years-old, working in the bakery based in Krefeld" recalls Eveline. *"This is where we produced the pies, bread rolls and even wedding cakes solely for NAAFI establishments, which in those days was approximately 100 clubs and 100 shops. We had 84 staff working and only four telephones so you can imagine how hectic life was, especially as we had to order all the ingredients, sort out all the invoices for production, wages, as well as making sure the goods went out accordingly! Our orders were making a value of 200,000 Deutsch Marks a week so on top of all this we also had to calculate all the profits by hand which was very tiresome believe me! I did this for 24 years and took over the bakery office shortly after the previous chief clerk retired."*

In 1986 the bakery closed due to the move to Kempen and the decision to source goods from the British Bakeries UK.

"The closing of the bakery was a difficult time for all of us, mainly because we had all put so much hard work into it! To me though, it was literally my world as I had worked there since I was 17! After the bakery closed down I worked in the buying office on the 'Berlin Budget'. The Berlin Budget involved the German Senate giving us approximately one million Deutsch Marks per year to allocate to NAAFI establishments all over Germany and included items such as cutlery, furnishings, cars and repairs."

During her 45 years with NAAFI, Eveline has seen a lot of change, including the fall of the Berlin Wall:

"Over the years I think the NAAFI has changed drastically. As well as the obvious development of technology, I especially remember the fall of the Berlin Wall. When Germany lost the war, Berlin was split in four parts to the winners - America, France, England and Russia. Russia claimed the largest part of Germany and controlled the border. Berlin was isolated in the middle of East Germany. People living in the East sector of Berlin tried to escape to the West, so the Russians built a high wall through the middle of Berlin on 13th August 1961. NAAFI had shops and clubs in the British part and a huge NAAFI Supermarket was built. In 1989 people in the East of Berlin were in revolt and finally the wall came down, all borders opened and the Eastern section came back to Germany. There was no longer any reason for the British, Americans, French and Russians to stay, so NAAFI closed all the shops and clubs in Berlin - from there onwards, step-by-step, many other NAAFI sites closed in other parts of Germany.

"Memorable experiences with the NAAFI include the Imperial club at Krefeld, playing bingo on Saturday nights, trips out to the Mosel River and Amsterdam excursions at the weekend. Skiing in the German Alps in 1999 with fellow NAAFI colleagues also stands out in my mind and was great fun."

NATIONAL SERVICE ABOLISHED

In 1957 the British Government abolished National Service and the strength of the Armed Forces was to be reduced to 375,000, virtually halving NAAFI's customers. It was the first time in 37 years that the profit was insufficient to meet obligations, although £3m in discounts and rebates were still paid to the Forces.

By the end of 1957 the focus of NAAFI's overseas operations had now changed completely. Egypt was out of the picture, Korea was now at peace and the Malayan emergency over. Cyprus now assumed centre stage.

In many countries, NAAFI helped the local economy and Cyprus was no different. A third of all NAAFI goods were bought locally and local industry was encouraged. The NAAFI seal of approval was regarded by shopkeepers as something approaching the Royal Warrant and NAAFI even contributed a member of the Cyprus Government when NAAFI Manager, John Mavrides, was elected to the House of Representatives.

Britain was trying to maintain the peace between a minority Turkish population and the Greek Cypriot backed EOKA guerrillas who were fighting for Greek supremacy on the island. The British troops were regarded as the enemy and men were advised not to turn their backs to the street unless accompanied by someone watching the passers-by. One in six of NAAFI's 1,500 employees was a Greek Cypriot and the risk of hostile infiltration was always high.

Eventually it happened, and a time bomb concealed in a sofa in a NAAFI canteen exploded killing two RAF men and wounding others. Immediately, the RAF banned all 4,000 Greek Cypriots employed in their camps and chaos inevitably followed. Without their local employees, 46 canteens, 17 shops and three clubs came to a standstill and an emergency appeal went out in Britain for 500 NAAFI volunteers. Within four days there were 17,000 applicants with 300 immediately selected to fly out to the war zone.

THE WINDS OF CHANGE

By the beginning of the 1960s the improvements in welfare and incomes, which began soon after the end of the war, started to transform the lives of people all over Europe, and servicemen were no exception. When an Army Sergeant stationed in Germany could call in at a NAAFI shop, order a car and pay for it in cash, it was time to realise that the organisation was no longer simply the grocer and victualler of the Armed Forces.

As NAAFI marked 40 years of service with new uniforms and a new crest, questions began to be asked about the future. Was NAAFI necessary when there was no major war? The 1961 Corbett Report confirmed that there was a definite need for NAAFI to continue to operate wherever and whenever the Armed Forces needed them. During the first 40 years the organisation had given almost £122m to the three Services in rebate, in spite of the known but often forgotten fact that some parts of the operation would never be profitable.

It was in the early 1960s when a new kind of NAAFI club was born, competing on equal terms with the pubs and clubs which began to mushroom in Garrison towns. Australian journalist, Howard D Murphet, a wartime soldier who remembered NAAFI from the Western Desert, described some of the changes he found when he revisited England and the new NAAFI clubs:

"Sailors, soldiers and airmen were reclining sleepily in big, soft armchairs or wandering across the carpet to order a whisky and soda at the bar. This vision of clubs for the rank and the file, equal to and better than the famous West End clubs enjoyed by the privileged few could have remained just a sailor's dream. But thanks to forward thinking by NAAFI, it materialised."

By the mid 1960s the image of NAAFI had been transformed. Modern supermarkets sold not just food and drink, but also kitchenware, clothes and electrical goods. Six hundred tons of goods poured out of the Krefeld warehouse every week and NAAFI even employed a sausage inspector to come over from Britain and teach German producers how to make proper British bangers! As lifestyles changed, NAAFI moved along with them to offer an ever wider range of services - petrol stations and bowling alleys as well as motor and life insurance.

By 1970, NAAFI the shopkeeper had taken over from NAAFI the caterer. To those who remembered NAAFI from the days of 'char and wad' in homely but bare barrack canteens, the progress made by the end of the 1960s would have seemed unbelievable.

A wave of nostalgia in the national press greeted NAAFI's 50th anniversary with the headlines reading, "Roll out the Barrel", "Fall out the Char and Wad Squad" and "End of an Era as NAAFI bury Char and Wad image".

NAAFI was now a huge business.

Image courtesy of the Council of the National Army Museum, London.

DO NOT GRAB

SPORTS BROADCASTER AND FORMER FOOTBALLER
GARY LINEKER OBE

DANGER

"I'm delighted to send my best wishes and congratulations to you all at NAAFI on your 90th year. I visited Afghanistan last year and having been caught up in a Taliban attack I discovered pretty quickly you need a place to unwind and NAAFI certainly provides that.

When you see the age of some of these guys on the front line you realise just how young some of them are and in NAAFI they have a place where they can escape the pressures of war and be reminded of home, whether it be a cup of NAAFI tea or a place to relax with their friends. You're all doing a great job and I wish you all every success for the future."

TROUBLE IN NORTHERN IRELAND

The emergency in Northern Ireland erupted in August 1969 after ten months of uneasy rumblings. By June 1972, there were 15,000 British soldiers in the province, six times more than there had been three years earlier. Without the willing offers of help from many former staff in Northern Ireland, both catholic and protestant, NAAFI would have found it impossible to cope.

In the Spring of 1972, 40 tons of goods a week were being moved, ranging from salt and pepper to haggis and smoked salmon. There were constant problems - deliveries, always in plain vans, had to pass through Army road blocks and rubble strewn streets; incoming letters and packets had to be x-rayed and shops and canteens had to cope with the sudden influx (and then disappearance) of troops on a daily basis.

The threat of danger was always there and on one occasion a box of soap found in one of the lavatories at Palace Barracks, Holywood was found by one NAAFI staff member to contain gelignite. There were many bomb threats and it was difficult for Club Managers in places like Lisburn to keep their staff. Many retired NAAFI staff stepped into the breach and offered their help on a part-time basis. As the months stretched into years, only the presence of British soldiers prevented the tension from the two communities exploding into civil war. In the meantime, NAAFI continued to do what it had always done best, helping to make conditions more bearable for the troops.

As well as staffing issues, NAAFI was to face yet more problems. At the time NAAFI had been serving the 3,000 British resident Forces and their families in six Barracks throughout the Province. However, at the outbreak of the troubles there was no declaration of conflict and, as Northern Ireland is part of the United Kingdom, NAAFI's uniformed EFI staff were prohibited from serving there. Given the situation, it was thought that NAAFI would not be able to respond quickly enough to serve Forces in difficult operational areas. This perception was wrong, as was later proved by the service provided in the Falklands Conflict and the Gulf War, but units moving to Northern Ireland began to strike up contracts with 'Sutlers' (independent traders or 'Charwallahs') who moved with them to the Province for the duration of their tour. These Sutlers were usually small businessmen who exploited difficult situations for their own profit, with quality standards usually coming low down on their list of priorities.

From small beginnings where Sutlers served alongside the British Forces in forward areas, a whole variety of services were soon competing with NAAFI throughout Northern Ireland. They eventually numbered more than 40 and were perceived to have two advantages over NAAFI. The first advantage was flexibility and the second was cash returned to the units. As the emergency moved on through the 1970s and into the early 1980s, doubts began to emerge as to the true value of the Sutlers services. The flexible friend was found to be not so flexible; hours of opening were limited and the standard of service and of hygiene in particular was often terrible. When coupled with allegations of bribery, high prices and an inflated end of month bill, the soldier seemed to be paying dearly in every aspect for a poor service. It was a repeat performance of what had happened during the First World War which had led to the establishment of NAAFI in the first place.

Whilst this was happening, NAAFI on the other hand had once again proved its ability to be flexible, with NAAFI Junior Ranks Clubs opening from 7am to midnight seven days a week. At the time of the mass breakout from the Maze Prison, NAAFI provided a non-stop service to the Prison Guard Force with the shop and food running for 60 hours continuously. Business phones were made continuously available and it was the NAAFI girls who visited the injured in hospital at Christmas armed with free magazines and beer.

Growing concerns over the Sutlers activities, coupled with an appreciation of the NAAFI service, led to an agreement under which NAAFI would gradually replace the Sutlers. This was a complete success and came with the added bonus that NAAFI's return of revenue to the units was at a higher rate than that of the Sutlers.

Once again NAAFI had proved its worth, although so widespread had been the use of the Sutlers that it took until 1992 to complete the programme.

CHIEF OF THE GENERAL STAFF
GENERAL SIR PETER WALL KCB CBE ADC

ESTABLISHED IN 1920, NAAFI CONTINUES TO LIVE UP ITS MOTTO OF *'SERVING THE SERVICES'*.

Integral to forces life, NAAFI provides much needed welfare support to Navy, Army and Air Force personnel wherever they are based in the world - a taste of home to make their time away from their family a little more bearable.

In this the 90th year since NAAFI's inception, we should recognise the commitment, dedication and sacrifice NAAFI staff past and present have made, and pay particular homage to those currently deployed in Afghanistan. On behalf of all three services, thank you NAAFI. We look forward to another 90 years!

THE DIAMOND JUBILEE

Back in the UK, the steady addition of new financial services and improvements to clubs and shops was continuing. As NAAFI marked its Diamond Jubilee in 1981, the first building society office was opened in Germany for British Service men and women. The pilot scheme was run with Abbey National and offered all kinds of savings accounts and specially tailored mortgages on UK properties. On the first day of operation, 58 new accounts were opened at Rheindahlen and over £33,000 paid in.

Meanwhile the NAAFI club scene was now as wide and varied as the tastes of those it catered for; there was a new look Pegasus Club at RAF Lyneham, brand new Imperial Clubs at Kennington and Nottingham, and a take-away snack bar at the Guards Depot, Pirbright. Throughout, NAAFI remained ever ready to meet any emergency, although few could have predicted at the beginning of 1982 that the biggest logistical challenge since World War II was only three months away.

THE FALKLANDS WAR - TO THE SOUTH ATLANTIC, QUICK MARCH!

NAAFI's most urgent task since the Suez crisis began late on Friday 2nd April 1982. The Argentineans had invaded the Falkland Islands that morning and now a Task Force was to be sent in to liberate the islands. That same Friday evening, NAAFI was ordered to put provisions aboard the ships for the 8,000 mile journey to the South Atlantic.

Throughout Britain, NAAFI staff had four days to organise and load thousands of crates onto the ships before they sailed south, working around the clock to supply the Fleet with food and drink for messes and shipboard canteens. Many worked every day that April; for them there was no Easter weekend.

Every hour was used by suppliers to meet deadlines. At Devonport, a local sausage supplier was relaxing in the pub when word came that his help was needed; he left the pub, glass still in hand, to make sure the order went through immediately. The NAAFI buyer purchased over half a million eggs that same weekend and every available spud was loaded onto the ships of the Task Force.

Supplying an Army of 8,000 men on a distant island thousands of miles away from England and occupied by a hostile power was a new experience to virtually all of NAAFI's staff on board the ships. The first two EFI men to land on the Falkland Islands were Canteen Manager Dave Higton and his assistant who left HMS Invincible on 7th June to set up a Bulk Issue Store at Ajax Bay. It was the day when Land Forces Commander, Major General Jeremy Moore, made a final appeal to the Argentine Commander, General Menendez, to lay down arms.

Throughout the conflict, Dave kept a diary to describe the sort of conditions he and his small supply team had to deal with during their first days ashore:

Monday 7th June: Issued with cold weather clothing and transferred to Fort Grange which would provide essentials (soap, razor, toothpaste etc.) for 5,000 men for one week.

Thursday 10th June: Air raids at 14.00 and 17.30. Issued with Atropine injectors and tablets for defence against possible Argentine gas attacks. First loads sent ashore to landing zone at 'Red' Beach. Sea King dropped us with kit into muddy bog. Given hot tea, taken to BIS accommodation - old Nissen hut. No windows or doors and many roof panels missing because building next door was bombed by the Argentines. No movement of stores possible from landing zones as forklift trucks unable to work in the deep mud in the dark.

Friday 11th June: Slept on the floor with only ship's internal sleeping bags. Interrupted by rainstorm which froze around us. Searched for more suitable kit and fortunately found Colour Sergeant Sandy McLeod who I knew from HMS Hermes where he was Sergeant's Mess President. Our survival depends on the amount of help and kit he can provide. Given hot food, camp beds, bed rolls, Arctic sleeping bags, boots, extra clothing, mess tins, sheets for the roof and much survival advice. Built temporary 'house' inside using mineral cases and kip sheets. First, and almost successful, attempt at cooking hot meal. Pressure from shore to obtain further stores, particularly cigarettes and chocolate. Surprise expressed about non-availability of beer and spirits. Electric light fitted, a welcome bonus for finding and checking stock, through outside generator. Check landing zone for one pallet of minerals still on hill. Stores OK but Higton and Chris Foulkard blown into mud by helicopter! Two dubious visits by customers, who left rapidly on finding we were sleeping with our stores!

Saturday 12th June: Find, to our delight, that an old hospital building 12 feet away from us contains two unexploded bombs, one suspended by parachute through a hole in the wall. Many casualties flown into field hospital. Overnight snow.

Sunday 13th June: Two red alerts during afternoon. Virtually all stores except soap, toothpaste and minerals exhausted.

Monday 14th June: Usual Force 10 gale through end of hut reduced to Force 5 by rebuilding wall and blocking off door. Argentinean prisoners start to arrive.

Wednesday 16th June: No loads sent forward. No transport. Heard Argentineans have surrendered Falklands but to expect air attacks from disgruntled Argentine Air Force. Fresh chops for supper courtesy of Colour Sergeant McLeod. At last a bottle of whiskey from HMS Fearless. Several hot toddies make us feel warm enough to go to sleep.

Wednesday 21st June: Flown back to Invincible. We both consider the time on the Falklands as well spent despite the atrocious conditions. About £11,000 worth of stock sold before more EFI staff arrived. Have learnt much, particularly about survival. Although confusion reigned from the first, the sense of achievement against all odds is extremely gratifying.

While diary extracts indicate the type of conditions experienced by NAAFI ashore and the sort of humour necessary to do their job, NAAFI staff who were afloat experienced the sinking of HMS Sheffield, HMS Coventry, HMS Ardent and HMS Antelope, as well as the HMS Atlantic Conveyor.

JIM MALLINSON'S FAMILY HAS SERVED IN THE ARMED FORCES SINCE 1820, FROM THE SIEGE OF MONTEVIDEO IN 1823 AND THE TWO WORLD WARS, TO THE FALKLANDS AND THEN AFGHANISTAN WHERE HIS BROTHER IS CURRENTLY SERVING.

JIM MALLINSON

"My own dealings with the NAAFI started, as most did, when I signed up with the Armed Forces in 1980. We were taken round the camp, shown everything, issued kit and when we got to the NAAFI we were told "right lads, NAAFI; if it don't sell it you don't need it".

The shop bar and van were all integral to Army life; I well remember drilling on the parade square in the pouring rain and waiting for that all important command - "NAAFI Break, fall out!" - and then the mad rush as we all tried to be the first in line for a cuppa, a bun and a fag! Sheltering under a tree and waiting for the NCO's to start shouting again, we all savoured those treats, and for a moment it was a haven of peace and temporary tranquillity.

After joining my regiment (17th Port and Maritime RCT), the NAAFI on camp was a real focal point; there was a shop, bar, TV, telephones, pool and snooker (all long before mobile phones, portable music and TV).

During the Falklands conflict I worked on port operations, moving cargo from ship to shore, and fuel ammunition. Very soon after the war ended, NAAFI decamped off the ships and took over a local shop. It became an instant hit with the troops, many of whom had been living in extreme conditions up in the hills and mountains around Stanley.

I can't describe the pleasure of sitting down on the wall outside the NAAFI and chomping my way through a Mars bar and guzzling cans of Coke after ages living on compo rations. It was sheer bliss! And we took it all for granted; we were here, so obviously NAAFI would be as well.

All through my military career NAAFI was part and parcel of the set up. If you went to the ranges the NAAFI wagon would turn up; 10 o'clock in the morning working in the port, NAAFI would be there with the wagon; midday to midnight, beer, fags, TV, boot polish was only a short walk out of the accommodation and across to the NAAFI.

Since I started working for the organisation I have seen a lot of changes; downsizing, restructure, new systems and new ideas. However, the overriding thing for me is knowing how important the NAAFI was during my time in the military and I know what it means to have that bit of home from home comfort. I might have taken it for granted back then but I and many others would have been much worse off if the NAAFI hadn't been there.

If me doing my job means some squaddie somewhere in the world can take a break, have a cuppa and a bun and relax for five minutes, then I'm happy."

01GF 54

NAAFI attached tremendous importance to the Falklands operation. Once hostilities were over, NAAFI consolidated their operations and 18 EFI staff were stationed in the Falklands. Games, sports equipment, radios and music tapes could now be added to the shipments of supplies. The original BIS set up at San Carlos was transferred after the ceasefire to Port Stanley and a small temporary shop opened seven days a week. Two purpose-built mobile refreshment vans were soon in operation too and canteens were established on the troop ships St. Edmund and the Rangatira.

One of the most unexpected problems after the ceasefire was the congestion on what had been one of the emptiest landscapes in the world. The enormous amount of plant and equipment on the island made parking, in the words of one Officer, *"as bad as London in the rail strike"*. The weather also played havoc with the delivery of supplies. During the frequent high winds, ships had to put out to sea for safety and any goods urgently needed were lifted ashore by helicopter.

During the period following the Falklands campaign, British troops remained on the Islands in large numbers. Far from home and in bleak surroundings, the troops found what NAAFI had always provided - warmth and companionship, bars, snacks and amusements. There was a shop selling gifts, electrical and sports goods and a full catalogue service enabling gifts to be sent out to the islands or back home. One of the most popular souvenirs was a soft toy penguin - made in the UK, sold in the Falklands and then taken back home again in due course!

Over 100 NAAFI staff who served with the Task Force for 30 days or more between April and June were awarded the South Atlantic Medal. NAAFI Canteen Manager John Leake also received the Distinguished Service Medal for leading a team of machine gunners aboard HMS Ardent whilst Graham Lloyd, Assistant Manager of Warehousing, and Irene Bardsley, Canteen Manager of HMS Excellent, won an MBE and British Empire Medal respectively, the former for co-ordinating the efforts of hundreds of staff.

The Falklands conflict had brought victory and honour to the British Forces and a triumph of logistics for NAAFI. However, back home there were other problems to face as Britain battled against recession.

A new phrase 'market forces' entered the vocabulary. Never before had NAAFI faced so much competition in both retail and service operations. The nub of the problem was always the same; NAAFI could only sell to the Service community and their spending power had been cut. When the head of a family was overseas for a six-month tour, spending could drop by as much as two thirds, as families went home for the duration and dropped out of the NAAFI net all together.

After 62 years of complaints that NAAFI prices were too high, a shopping survey published by the Daily Star in 1983 showed that, after discount, NAAFI came fifth in the national league table of supermarket chains. A year later, Service wives at Tidworth did their own survey and confirmed that NAAFI prices were on a par with Tesco and Safeway.

COLD WAR

It was during the 1980s and the height of the Cold War that EFI was involved in a number of major British and NATO exercises. One of their biggest tests came in Germany during Exercise Lionheart in 1984 when NAAFI, including 86 EFI plus civilian staff, looked after over 50,000 regular and reserve troops from the UK in appalling weather conditions - the biggest peace time troop movement since World War II.

Three years later, a 25-strong EFI team experienced the full rigours of arctic training during a 10-week exercise in Norway for 5,500 Royal Marines and troops of the Allied Command Europe (Mobile) Force. Sleeping in tents, they experienced long dark nights in sub-zero temperatures where survival in the freezing conditions tested every aspect of their training. Temperatures were so low that men could only work outside in 15-minute shifts.

The Naval Canteen Service also played a vital role when British nationals and men, women and children from 50 other countries had to be evacuated from Aden when the South Yemeni Government was overthrown by Marxist rebels in 1986. The Royal Yacht Britannia was the only ship allowed inside South Yemeni territorial waters and NAAFI Canteen Manager Dave Atkinson and his assistant served over 3,000 cups of tea, 9,000 biscuits and over 1,000 hot meals before their charges were evacuated to other Royal Navy ships.

63

THE GULF WAR… AND THE AFTERMATH

No sooner had the Iron Curtain been lifted and the last blocks of the Berlin Wall sold as souvenirs than a new dictator emerged to challenge the new world order.

On 2nd August 1990, Saddam Hussein, ruler of Iraq, invaded Kuwait - the consequences of his action involving over 600,000 troops from 29 nations. Within five days there were 50 warships converging on the Gulf, including one British destroyer, two frigates and a support ship. A day later the first American troops arrived in Saudi Arabia and on 10th August Operation Granby got underway in Britain.

NAAFI called for volunteers. 60 immediately came forward for Gulf service from NAAFI shops, clubs, warehouses and offices in Britain and Germany. The first nine-man EFI team left for the Gulf after a period of concentrated military training, confident that they could do their job well and with the ability to react in the event of a biological or chemical attack. Their personal kit weighed in at 80lbs including lightweight combat gear, water bottles, emergency rations, S10 respirators and NBC suits. With the first EFI team was Warrant Officer Dave Forster:

"We landed at Al Jubail Military Airfield in the early morning. At the fort we were issued with our weapons and live rounds; everyone was expecting action at any time. We hardly had time to arrive before we set to work, calling forward the NAAFI containers, checking off the stock and virtually issuing it at the same time. An average day would be 18 hours; during the day we would be setting up the Bulk Issue Store and shop, running mobile canteens down to the docks for the arrival of the new troops and taking stock out during the evening for the units already in the desert."

In the desert, the EFI teams had set up and were running four Bulk Issue Stores and two 24-hour tented shops. Mobile services were being provided using Army DROPS vehicles and Land Rovers, plus a converted refrigerated container which was used to sell cold drinks which were in constant demand. As soon as it appeared hundreds of soldiers, including Americans, would emerge from the trenches.

During the period leading up to the conflict, EFI staff had worked round the clock supplying servicemen with over two million packets of sweets and chocolates, 300,000 packets of biscuits, 320,000 tablets of soap, 120,000 tubes of toothpaste, two million razor blades, 60,000 bottles of shampoo and 80,000 writing pads! £32,000 worth of flowers were also sent home by British troops in the Gulf using NAAFI's Interflora service. The only traditional item missing at Christmas was alcohol, which was banned in Saudi Arabia.

Whilst EFI were supporting the troops on the ground, NCS were supporting the Royal Navy at sea. Brian Whitaker was one of 20 NAAFI Canteen Managers serving with Royal Navy ships in the conflict zone, where hostilities ended after 197 days at sea. His ship, HMS London, went into action early when she intercepted an Iraqi merchant ship under the UN Trade Embargo. As a first aider during Action Stations, Brian did not see daylight for six weeks, with the canteen open for 19 hours a day.

Barely was the ink dry from the signing of the ceasefire agreement that the world was shocked by the plight of hundreds of thousands of Kurdish refugees, driven out of their homes in northern Iraq by Saddam Hussein's army. Eleven NAAFI volunteers flew out to northern Iraq on 1st May to serve the British Royal Marine Commandos and RAF Support Teams who were guarding the Kurdish refugees in the safe havens established by the British and French. The objectives of the Marines on Operation Safe Haven were two-fold. The first was to help lead the refugees down from the mountains to the safe havens; the second was to ensure that they would be safe when returning to their homes. To achieve this most Marines were deployed in forward positions in Iraq and a Bulk Issue Store was set up near Sirsank airfield before they arrived. NAAFI's Managing Director at the time, Brigadier James Rucker, told EFI volunteers that they would be taking part 'in one of the most humanitarian operations we have ever done'.

During Operation Safe Haven conditions for everyone were basic. The camp occupied a vast plain of dust and stones and was plagued with flies. Other pests included scorpions and camel spiders, both of which had venomous bites. There were no showers and only field toilets, whilst meals were 'boil-in-the-bag' ranging from spaghetti bolognaise to omelettes and savoury rice. Everyone experienced frequent stomach problems.

When the EFI team returned home, it was a long time before they forgot the images of Northern Iraq; the desolate villages, the sprawling refugee camps, families mourning the loss of loved ones and the urgent pleadings of the Kurds to the Allied Forces to stay. Even so, Operation Safe Haven was one of NAAFI's proudest missions; they had seen children smiling and waving again - and above all else, alive.

The Gulf War land campaign ended after 100 hours of fierce fighting.

Alongside the soldiers - and only 10km from the Kuwait border when the ground war started - EFI faced scud missile attack and air raid warnings, dug trenches, filled sandbags and carried their weapons and gas masks at all times.

FOOTBALLER AND SPORTS PERSONALITY
DAVID BECKHAM OBE

> "I've represented my country many times on the field, but what our Armed Forces do representing our country is really amazing. They are the bravest people I've ever met and are so focused on their job you can see it in their eyes. These men and women leave their family and friends behind to do their jobs, but when you see the morale of the troops out here it really is incredible, and more often than not that's down to the NAAFI.
>
> During my recent visit, the NAAFI provided all those home comforts when they are needed most, whilst the NAAFI staff who come out to serve the troops in places like Afghanistan provide real life support. It takes a special kind of person to do that and I have nothing but respect for the organisation and the unique support it continues to give our Forces around the world. Congratulations on your 90th year."

THE BALKANS CONFLICT

By the time of its 75th anniversary, NAAFI had returned over £412m in rebates and discounts to the Navy, Army and Air Forces.

The Cold War was in the past but NAAFI yet again had to examine the future as the MOD's 'Options for Change' slashed the size of Britain's Armed Forces.

By the early 1990s, thousands of servicemen and their families were coming back from Germany and many left for new careers in Civvy Street. However, before the last remaining EFI staff returned from the Gulf and Kurdistan in 1991, the beginnings of a new and bitter conflict had exploded in former Yugoslavia.

On 25th June 1992 Croatia and Slovenia declared themselves independent of the Federation. Battles were fought between the Yugoslav Peoples' Army, under the Federal Government in Belgrade, and the Slovenian Territorial Defence Force. Later that year British troops were deployed to support the United Nations Protection Force, which was sent to guard convoys bringing aid to the stricken population. The first two members of EFI arrived in Plesno airbase near Zagreb during the summer and although the fighting in Croatia was over, thousands of unexploded mines ensured that the danger remained.

The Bulk Issue Store at Plesno sold beer, spirits and other items in bulk to individual units, catering for all of the eight countries taking part in the UN operation. Soldiers from the Kenyan battalion were keen to buy cameras and videos whilst the Canadians ordered industrial washing machines and tumble dryers.

Once again NAAFI continued to provide that taste of home when it was needed most.

IRAQ AND THE FALL OF SADDAM HUSSEIN

The Iraq War began on 20th March 2003 with the invasion of Iraq by a multinational force led by the United States and the United Kingdom. During this initial invasion phase, the US and UK were joined by troops from Australia and Poland, whilst 36 other countries were involved in its aftermath.

In preparation for the invasion, NAAFI staff deployed to Kuwait. EFI set up a logistics base in Shaiba, operating out of a RDS (Rapid Deployment System) unit, and a warehouse at the port in Kuwait so that the EFI detachments could be supplied more easily.

When the troops eventually pushed forward into Iraq, EFI followed closely behind. Stock was moved any way it could, with EFI staff driving back and forth to the warehouse and offloading up to six trucks by hand just to keep the camps supplied with soft drinks and anything else the troops needed.

At its height during the early stages of the invasion, the number of British troops in Iraq numbered some 46,000 but after the initial invasion this number dropped to 8,500. By the end of 2003 the EFI warehouse in Kuwait closed and reopened in Shaiba, with detachments at both Basrah Palace and Shatt-Al-Arab Hotel.

The invasion of Iraq led to an occupation and the eventual capture of Saddam Hussein, who was later tried in an Iraqi court of law and executed by the new Iraqi government. Throughout the Iraq conflict, NAAFI had provided shops and cafes in Camp Centurian, Camp Fox and Camp Beuhring, as well as supplying welfare villages in Basrah and Umm Qsar.

For NAAFI civilian staff who were recruited from Bosnia and Germany, working in Iraq was a daunting prospect and at times extremely frightening. However, every member of EFI carried out their duties professionally, taking the constant threat of mortar and rocket attacks in their stride.

UK forces ended combat operations on 30th April 2009 with members of EFI amongst the last remaining people to exit the war-torn country.

NAAFI closed its final establishment in Camp Beuhring three months later in August 2009.

AFTER LEAVING SCHOOL AT THE TENDER AGE OF 15, BOB BEGAN HIS WORKING LIFE AS A SHOP ASSISTANT FOR GALBRAITHS, BEFORE DECIDING ON A CAREER WITH NAAFI FIVE YEARS LATER IN AUGUST 1972. WITH NO PREVIOUS EXPERIENCE IN WORKING WITH THE MILITARY, BOB SPENT HIS FIRST THREE MONTHS BASED AT RAF NEWTON, BEFORE MOVING TO GERMANY WHERE HE REMAINED FOR THE NEXT 16 YEARS.

BOB MCCALL

"From 1972 to 1988 I was based in numerous locations around Germany, moving around the country every two or three years from one shop to the other, resulting in a fair share of dramatic experiences" says Bob. *"In one particular instance we had a hostage situation, which was treated very seriously by the Armed German Police who called the Anti Terrorist Unit out. We received a phone call at the shopping complex in Gütersloh on a busy Saturday morning to say that the official in charge had been taken hostage and we were to take all the money out of the safe and deliver it to a specified location. As we made our way to the drop off point, I remember sitting in the passenger seat of the company car writing down the serial numbers of 100DM notes so they could be traced. As NAAFI staff we were instructed by the police to do exactly as we had been told. Luckily, this turned out to be a hoax, but we had to treat it with severe caution just in case it was real, making it an experience which will remain one of my most memorable."*

After several years in a job, many people find themselves itching for a new career, but Bob is just as proud to be working for NAAFI today as he was then, finding the role just as rewarding. Today, he's based in Faslane Naval Base, 25 miles from Glasgow and still talks with enthusiasm about his role. He states that no two days are ever the same - a simple phone call, fax or e-mail can change the way a whole day turns out, providing new and exciting challenges.

"NAAFI is such a unique organisation to work for. If you speak to anyone who has worked for NAAFI for any amount of time they will tell you all about the feeling of belonging, being part of the big family. My son Justin and daughter Lindsay have both worked for NAAFI!

My current position as the Manager of the NAAFI Ships Transit at the Faslane base allows me to meet so many new faces. Throughout the years, I've been privileged enough to meet all kinds of interesting people, whether it be staff or customers, which adds so much variation and character to my job. It's the characters that I have met over the years that have made working for NAAFI so special. I've really made some great friends for life.

From the fall of the Berlin Wall and our exit from Cyprus, to the war in Iraq and the current war in Afghanistan, I've seen these changes first-hand and its direct effect on NAAFI activity. However, NAAFI has always managed to successfully adapt and continue to boost morale, even in the most trying circumstances. NAAFI is my life and something that gets in your blood. It's all I've ever known and I wouldn't have it any other way."

THE WAR IN AFGHANISTAN

Since 1921, NAAFI has actively supported Britain's Armed Forces, side by side, in campaigns all around the world, something it continues to do today in Afghanistan.

The war in Afghanistan began on 7th October 2001 in response to the September 11th attacks on the United States of America. On that fateful day, almost 3,000 people were killed in attacks on the World Trade Centre and the Pentagon by hijacked civilian airliners. Another hijacked aircraft crashed in a field after crew and passengers attempted to seize control of the plane.

The attacks were quickly linked to Al-Qaeda and less than one week after the events of September 11th, then U.S. President George W. Bush identified Osama Bin Laden as the prime suspect in the attacks.

After the refusal of the Taliban regime to cease harbouring Al-Qaeda, the U.S. Government launched military operations in Afghanistan, with the UK leading its own military operation, Operation Herrick, in support.

NAAFI set up a shop and Bulk Issue Store in Camp Souter, Kabul, with a further shop and cafe/bar set up in ISAF, the NATO base. Outlets in forward locations such as Kandahar, Gereshk and Lash Ka Gar followed before NAAFI opened up a number of facilities in Camp Bastion, including a pizza and Indian takeaway. A restaurant was also opened in Kandahar.

The Bulk Issue Store also moved down to Camp Bastion and, for those units who worked too far away from the shops, NAAFI ran a mobile EFI van in both Camp Bastion and Kandahar to take cold drinks and sweets out to the troops.

In 2007 a new coffee shop was built in Kandahar; this was the first of a number of 'high street' style cafes to open in a Forward Operating Base (FOB) where troops could relax and enjoy a freshly brewed cup of tea, in air-conditioned facilities, with leather-bound seats. When FOB Jackson opened in early 2010 NAAFI was there again, sending in a RDS unit with two uniformed EFI staff to run it.

Today the war in Afghanistan goes on, and NAAFI continue to support our brave men and women with all the comforts of home, providing that respite and link to normality when it is needed most.

ACTOR AND AWARD-WINNING PRESENTER

ROSS KEMP

"

"NAAFI isn't just a place where people come and get a respite from conflict they are involved in, it's a place that gives them a taste and feel of home.

It is difficult to understand a war zone unless you have actually been to one. We were just out there for a very short period of time, whereas soldiers spend six or seven months there. The one thing you look forward to while you are out there is getting back to the NAAFI and to the good things it provides.

Like the British Armed Forces, the men and women of NAAFI who volunteer to work out in places like Afghanistan do a tremendous job for the good of this country and I wish you all the very best on your 90th year."

MAJOR LYNN CASSIDY WAS NAAFI COUNTRY MANAGER IN AFGHANISTAN UNTIL 2008, HAVING COMPLETED TEN OPERATIONAL TOURS, INCLUDING FIVE TOURS OF IRAQ AND THREE OF AFGHANISTAN.

MAJOR LYNN CASSIDY

"Working with EFI has been the best experience of my life," says Lynn. *"After starting my NAAFI career as a Manager in Celle, Germany, I enrolled within EFI, the uniformed arm of NAAFI working alongside troops on the front line, in 2000. What we do gives so much to you as a person and so much to the guys I can't express it enough. I feel privileged to serve our Service men and women fighting on the front line with the home comforts that make their job just that little bit easier."*

Lynn describes herself as a 'people person' and that's what working for NAAFI is all about: *"Serving the Services is at the heart of everything we do and the ability to get on with people is key to the role. Working in a retail environment in a place like Afghanistan is like nothing else. It is such a sociable job. There's always that feeling that you can go that extra mile to help the efforts out there and show the active Service men and women that we are grateful for their commitment whether that be on the frontline in Afghanistan or places that people tend to forget about like the Falklands, Germany or Northern Ireland. Just being there to serve the troops, I really get the feeling that they appreciate we are there helping them to do their jobs and give them a little slice of home."*

The Armed Forces is an integral part of Lynn's life. Married to a soldier and with two soldier sons aged 25 and 27, military life is in her blood and, Lynn believes, probably always will be. She says: *"My world revolves around Force's life and I really identify with the troops in theatre. As the mother of two serving soldiers I can speak from experience when I say how important it is for the troops out in Afghanistan to have someone to turn to or chat to over a cup of tea. It's the simplest of things that make a real difference. Being on the front line can be a very lonely place especially when your loved ones are thousands of miles away."*

Although Lynn says she has never felt in danger while she's been serving, she has had one or two near misses and it's always at the back of her mind. On one occasion she was part of a rolling convoy on its way back from Kuwait when one of the vehicles was hit by an IED (Improvised Explosive Device). She says: *"While that incident was terrifying you can't let it affect you. I just had to put it to the back of my mind and think about the risks that the guys on the front line take every minute they are out there. I just had to get on with it and do my job. Like they do, day in day out!"*

Lynn says that NAAFI life presents the same challenges as any normal retail environment, and a few more: *"My first time in Kuwait in 2003, I was trading out of an 18ft x 24ft tent from a trestle table in the middle of the desert. The conditions were incredibly challenging but this was at the start of the second Gulf war so was a key time. I was out there for six months and it was probably at this time that the realisation of the importance of my role dawned on me. I knew that I was doing the job that I was born to do."*

When it comes to the future, Lynn is quite happy to remain on the operational side of things and is now Commanding Officer based in Grantham. Lynn, who wanted to be a policewoman when she was a little girl, lives in Hertfordshire and particularly enjoys the training element of her latest role.

She says: *"While there is still a war on it's vital that we in NAAFI continue to recruit and train EFI personnel who can provide the required level of support and service to our troops. I've worked with a superb group of people in an organisation that has a long and proud history. NAAFI has given me and thousands of others a hugely rewarding career and I'm thrilled to be associated with it. NAAFI's contribution and the contribution of its staff, from those serving the Services on the front line to the behind the scenes team who keep everything moving, cannot be underestimated. It's amazing to think that NAAFI has been fulfilling such a valuable role for the past 90 years. Long may it continue!"*

HEROES

75

We're with you every step of the way

NAAFI

Serving the Services

90 YEARS ON... NOT THE FINAL CHAPTER

Whether serving tea to the soldiers in the Sudan in the 1920s, looking after the staff of Buckingham Palace in the thirties, or serving pilots at Fighter and Bomber RAF Stations during World War II, the story of NAAFI is an unforgettable one and NAAFI remains to this day a unique and very British institution.

It is hoped that the extraordinary stories told within this book will find a readership well beyond the bounds of those who made them and as a consequence, serve as an introduction to an organisation that has served Britain's Armed Forces for over 90 years.

As a trusted, experienced and committed British service provider of catering, retail and leisure facilities, NAAFI continue to work in partnership with the Armed Forces wherever there is a need, delivering that taste of home and moral boosting link to normality when it is needed most.

Here's to the next 90 years!

THE PRIME MINISTER

"Our Armed Forces are without doubt second to none. The courage and professionalism shown is legendary and I believe we can be justifiably proud of them all. However, behind every successful force there are many unsung heroes.

NAAFI, in its 90th year, has supported our Armed Forces throughout the world and in many arduous situations. I had the pleasure of visiting one of your facilities at Camp Bastion during my recent visit to Afghanistan and it was evident how much your facilities means to our Armed Forces.

I know you are held in the highest regard by the Service community and veterans alike and I would like to add my own congratulations on your 90th Anniversary. Those that have died in Service should be remembered but we should also celebrate your achievements. Our Service men and women know that, whatever they are asked to do, NAAFI will be with them."

David Cameron

A POSTSCRIPT FROM NAAFI CHAIRMAN, SIR IAN PROSSER

On the anniversary of our 90th year, it is fitting that we look back in admiration on our years of service to the Armed Forces and acknowledge the outstanding work and achievements of our predecessors. The history of The Navy, Army and Air Force Institutes is decorated with stories of courage, humour, self-sacrifice and sometimes tragedy all around the world, yet wherever we go NAAFI remains a unique and very British institution.

Today NAAFI continues to provide a wide range of services, including catering, retail and leisure facilities in Germany, Afghanistan, Ascension Islands, the Falkland Islands, Brunei, Gibraltar and Northern Ireland, as well as on board all Royal Navy Ships.

As far as catering, retail and leisure businesses go, we're like no other. For us it's more than running shops and clubs; it's about making a huge difference to people who count on our services. For our staff, it's about more than just a job, but an opportunity to make that difference. In other words it's a chance to take on a career that really means something - to give true life support to the men and women who so bravely represent our country.

Always at the heart of NAAFI has been the dedication of its people, who continue to put service and loyalty at the top of their personal values. It's their commitment and drive that helps us deliver our service with a smile, often under extreme conditions. Since our inception in 1920, over 550 NAAFI employees have made the ultimate sacrifice for their country, losing their lives in conflicts all around the world. As we celebrate the history of NAAFI we also commemorate those who have lost their lives so bravely.

As a not for profit organisation, created and managed solely to serve the Services, 90 years on, NAAFI's sole purpose today is the same as it's always been - to support the British Armed Forces and their families, wherever they are deployed on operations or where they, or their families, are posted overseas.

Servitor Servientium; Serving those who Serve.

THANKS

'Celebrating 90 years of NAAFI *Serving the Services*' is told through its people, the Military, and all those who have had reason to be grateful for its service at one stage or another. We gratefully acknowledge this and thank each and every one of you, past and present, for your kind contributions.

A TRIBUTE FROM FORMER CHIEF OF THE DEFENCE STAFF,
SIR JOCK STIRRUP GCB AFC ADC DSC FRAES FCMI RAF

"I am delighted to have been given the opportunity to pay tribute to NAAFI in this its 90th Anniversary year. Ever since it was established in 1920, the NAAFI has been supporting Service personnel in both war and peace. It has provided welcome succour and sustenance in some of the world's most inhospitable environments. For very many years and for many millions of sailors, soldiers, and airmen it has indeed proved an 'institution'; a haven in which to relax and the chance for a chat and a welcome respite from the demands of war or work.

At its zenith, in 1945, NAAFI had over 110,000 staff serving with all three Services right across the globe. This tradition has continued throughout the many campaigns since the Second World War which have seen NAAFI personnel deploy supporting Service personnel in more than 45 countries across every continent. And it continues today with NAAFI personnel deployed to both Afghanistan and the Falkland Islands as well as more locally delivering catering, retail and leisure services to meet the expectations of today's Service personnel and their families. Those of us who are serving and those who have served owe a considerable debt of gratitude to all those within NAAFI who have served us with such distinction, courage and good humour. And most particularly it is right that at this time when we are celebrating 90 years of achievement we also remember the sacrifice of the 550 NAAFI staff who have died in Service."

FORMER CHIEF OF THE GENERAL STAFF,
GENERAL SIR RICHARD DANNATT GCB CBE MC

"NAAFI has supported the Armed Forces wonderfully over the 90 years of its history, both at home and overseas. All of us who have served, or are serving, and our families have benefited enormously from all that the NAAFI has provided, even in most difficult circumstances. Thank you for all you have done, and very best wishes for the future."

CEO AND CO-FOUNDER OF HELP FOR HEROES,
BRYN PARRY OBE

"NAAFI have a longstanding relationship with our Service men and women; we're delighted to have their support and would like to say thank you for all the fantastic work they've already done."

NAAFI PENSIONERS

In the year of our 90th anniversary, a total of 114 NAAFI pensioners also celebrated being aged 90 or over. NAAFI sees each and every employee, past and present, as part of the family and we are delighted to recognise such remarkable individuals on this most special occasion.

B M Austen	E L Dore	V S Lilly	E A Speaight
H H Aylen	T Edge	R A Lintott	D Steel
M E Baines	G Edwards	D M Mann	E F Strange
I H Baldwin	M C Edwardson	G M Marsh	L V Strickland
J W Barlow	R E Freeman	K P Matthews	A M Sullivan
J Beardsall	E George-Davidson	M E McCaffrey	M Talbot
V E Belcher	M M Giles	E I Mitchell	M Tester
I G Benstead	S M Gillatt	W M Munasinha	C M Thomson
R E Birkett	V F M Glibbery	M O Neville	F Travell
R W Boulton	E J Glinn	I M New	A W Trott
P Boundy	R F Gulliver	I M Nix	E M Trott
I P Branford	E H M Haick	L North	P M Utpadel
E C Burkart	G W Harnett	B Ondrus	E A Wakelin
D W Burke	H Harp	N G Penny	P L Walsh
T M Byrne	F Hayes	H P T Prideaux	C Webster
C E Campton	W T Healy	V K Ramakrishnan	G M Webster
H M Carrigan	J T Herron	J Rangecroft	E W Wheeler
L J Chapman	R J Hewlett	W A Rayney	H White
A T Clarke	I Hollow	A Redfern	R B Wijesinha
P Clarke	E M Holmes	D M Roberts	B T Willcocks
F R Clifford	M E Hopwood	E M Robinson	H S Witt
H E Collins	C D Horn	J Robinson	A W Wood
W S Coxhead	M J Hughes	M S Robinson	S Worby
C Crabtree	C James	I J Rogers	E Worth
A E Cross	A R Johnson	M L Sarkies	P O Worthington
I Cunningham	J D Keeler	F G Seaton	S A Wright
M M Dale	T Kilpatrick	H M Simpson	W J Yates
L J Davies	D Lacey	G W Singleton	
J W Dempster	L G Lesenger Bem	A Smith	

Ethel Holmes (92) and Maria Baines (90) celebrating at a Pensioners Reunion, held at the Victory Club in London, August 2010.